developing
Numeracy Skills

NUMERACY

KEY STAGE 2: YEAR 3/ PRIMARY 4

SUE ATKINSON
DIANA COBDEN

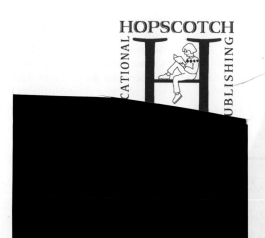

HOPSCOTCH
EDUCATIONAL PUBLISHING

Contents

Published by Hopscotch Educational Publishing Ltd,
Althorpe House, Althorpe Street, Leamington Spa CV31 2AU.

© 1999 Hopscotch Educational Publishing

Written by Sue Atkinson and Diana Cobden
Series design by Blade Communications
Illustrated by Jean de Lamos
Cover illustration by Claire Boyce
Printed by Clintplan, Southam

Sue Atkinson and Diana Cobden hereby assert their moral right
to be identified as the authors of this work in accordance with
the Copyright, Designs and Patents Act, 1988.

ISBN 1-902239-33-4

©Hopscotch Educational Publishing

Introduction

◆ ABOUT THE SERIES ◆

Developing Numeracy Skills is a series of books aimed at developing the basic skills of the 'Framework for teaching mathematics'. There is one book for each year from Reception (Scottish Primary 1), through Key Stage 1 to the end of Key Stage 2 (Scottish Primary 7).

The series offers a structured approach which provides detailed lesson plans to teach specific numeracy skills. A unique feature of the series is the provision of differentiated photocopiable activities which are aimed at considerably reducing teacher preparation time.

◆ ABOUT THIS BOOK ◆

This book is for teachers of Year 3 children and Scottish level P4. It aims to:

◆ give emphasis to those aspects of numeracy that teachers on the National Numeracy Project found to be crucial to raising the standards of numeracy in their classrooms
◆ support a three-fold structured lesson for maximising learning to raise standards
◆ support teachers in developing children's flexible methods of calculating
◆ encourage a wide range of mathematical vocabulary by giving some key questions to ask
◆ support teachers with a wide range of mental maths questions to develop good mental recall with children.

Throughout the book the maths is set in the context of a circus, but you can adapt the lessons by using your own topic.

You will find that the content for the other books for Years 3/P4 to Year 6/P7 in this series are structured in a similar way to assist you if you have a mixed age class. So if you have mixed 7- to 9-year-olds, you can use the Y4/P5 book alongside this one in order to develop different lessons that follow on from this book.

◆ CHAPTER CONTENT ◆

◆ Overall learning objectives

Each chapter has two lesson plans and the overall learning objectives outline the aims for both lessons and the further activities in each chapter.

◆ Assessment focus

This sets out the specific learning objective that you will be able to assess for each individual lesson within the chapter. (See page 4 for more on assessment.)

◆ Resources

This is a list of what you will need to do the lessons.

◆ Oral work and mental calculation

This section is a 'mental maths warm up' and can sometimes have a different learning objective from the main lesson plan. It gives you ideas for how to develop quick mental recall with your children, so keeping key ideas ticking over and giving them the extra practice they need to be confident. You can 'mix and match' these to suit your lesson. So, you might want to do multiplication of 5x and 10x every day for a week, even when your main lesson is about measuring, or you might want to recap something about addition on a day when the main lesson is about data handling, and so on. This section of the lesson would be between about five to ten minutes long.

◆ Starting point: whole class

This provides ideas for introducing the activity and may include key questions to ask the children so that they can move on to their group task having been introduced to concepts and the vocabulary they will need for the group activities. This starting point is usually about ten minutes long, depending on the task.

Introduction

◆ Group activities

This explains the tasks that the children will do. The 'Focus group' works with you and this group alternates between the different ability groups. The section on 'teacher-independent groups' gives three tasks that can be done more or less independently of you. Sometimes you might use only two of the three independent tasks because one group is the focus group. The Group 1 tasks are the easiest and the Group 3 tasks the hardest. For Year 3/P4 children, this section is about 15 or 25 minutes long, depending on the task. Some of these teacher-independent tasks are maths games. Games give plenty of practice with the learning objective, help children to learn the language associated with the concept you are teaching, and can provide the incentive to keep working while you are busy with your focus group.

◆ Using the differentiated activity sheets

Activity 1 is for the children who are likely to struggle with the content of the lesson and who need a simple task, often with lower numbers than other groups. Activity 2 is for children who seem to have grasped the main ideas during the whole class starter, and Activity 3 for those who need a more challenging task.

The book symbol at the bottom of some activity pages is for further work to be done in maths books.

◆ Plenary session

This suggests ideas for a whole-class review to discuss the learning outcomes and gives questions to ask so that children have a chance to reflect on what they have learned and for the teacher to assess. This section is usually about five to ten minutes.

◆ Further activities

This is a list of further activities that can be developed from the lessons to give children more experience with the learning objectives. Some of these use generic sheets at the back of the book and some could be used for homework.

◆ Extension

These are ideas for how to take children on and give them more difficult tasks.

◆ Support

These are ideas for children who are going to need more support before they have grasped the learning objectives.

◆ The use of calculators

Children will not be using calculators for mental calculations unless the intention is to free them from the time it takes to calculate when your objective is that they need to see a pattern. So, if you want children to see the pattern of multiplying a number by 10, doing this on a calculator will teach the child an enormous amount about place value that they might not learn from using an abacus, for example. Calculators are invaluable tools for teaching maths, just as cubes and place value boards are, but we must teach children to use them well. It is not a good use of calculators to use them repeatedly for checking, though this can be useful at times. Children need to check their work by doing the calculation in a different way, not resorting to keying in the numbers.

◆ GENERIC SHEETS ◆

There are some generic sheets at the back of the book that give extra help with key skills and can also be made into maths games. These sheets can be photocopied with different numbers on them to suit your different groups. Guidance on using them is given in the lesson plans or in the Further activities section.

◆ ASSESSMENT ◆

You will notice at the top of each activity sheet there is a row of three small boxes. These link with your assessment of how well the child has grasped the intended learning for that lesson. On page 5 there is a list of the assessment criteria for both lessons for each chapter (the ones for the activity sheets are in italics). You can use these criteria to decide how well a child has grasped the content of a particular lesson.

♦ If they seem not to have grasped the concept, tick the first box.

♦ If there is evidence of the child having learned what you intended, tick the second box.

♦ Tick the third box for children who have a very secure grasp of the lesson and you think can use and apply the concept.

Of course, there will often be no evidence on the sheet that corresponds with your observations of some children's understandings during oral maths times and when you work with your focus group. You will need to make a note (on the sheet if you want) of what those children said or did to back up why you ticked a particular box. We need to listen to children very carefully as they respond to the activity and we need to use prompting and probing questions in order to be clear about what each individual understands. Assessment is much broader than children's recordings, so your additional annotations based on your observations are important. At the end of each half term, flicking through each child's sheets can give you a basis for your teacher assessments, and will enable you to plan for your next half term.

In addition to this assessment on the children's sheets, there is a self assessment sheet on page 96. The blank spaces are for you and the child to record specific targets that the child has achieved. The children will need to reflect on their learning; for example, they need to think of a favourite way to add two-digit numbers and think about what they would like to be better at in maths.

Year 3 Assessment Criteria

Chapter 1
Can use grouping strategies to estimate sensibly and count accurately.
Can understand rounding to the nearest 10.

Chapter 2
Can describe and extend number sequences.
Can give a sensible estimate and check by counting.

Chapter 3
Can add or subtract 1, 10 or 100 from a given number.
Can order numbers up to 1000.

Chapter 4
Can understand and use the relationship between addition and subtraction.
Can understand addition can be done in any order and use a range of maths vocabulary.

Chapter 5
Can put the larger number first.
Can explain strategies for addition and subtraction on a number line.

Chapter 6
Can understand differences can be found by counting on or back.
Can use knowledge of subtract 10 in order to subtract 9 and 11.

Chapter 7
Can interpret real life situations where multiplication is needed.
Can use a range of language for multiplication.

Chapter 8
Can understand division is the inverse of multiplication.
Can use a range of vocabulary for division.

Chapter 9
Can understand whole number remainders.
Can make sensible decisions about rounding up or down.

Chapter 10
Can identify and name common fractions.
Can use a number line for fractions.

Chapter 11
Can recognise and use decimal notation in money.
Can solve problems with linear measurements.

Chapter 12
Can use equipment for linear measuring.
Can make reasonable estimates and check by measuring.

Chapter 13
Can use suitable units for measuring capacity.
Can read a variety of scales, labelled and unlabelled.

Chapter 14
Can interpret data and make predictions.
Can collect and represent data.

The criteria in italics are those that relate to the children's activity sheets.

Counting and rounding

◆ Overall learning objectives

✦ Count collections accurately by grouping in 2s, 5s and 10s.
✦ Make a tally to help with counting.
✦ Give sensible estimates of the number of items in a collection.
✦ Use, read and write the vocabulary for estimation and approximation.
✦ Round 2-digit numbers to the nearest ten and 3-digit numbers to the nearest hundred.
✦ Count on and back in 2s, 5s and 10s from any 2-digit number.

◆ LESSON ONE HOW MANY?

◆ Assessment focus

Can the children use grouping strategies to estimate sensibly and count accurately?

◆ Resources

✦ interlocking cubes
✦ number lines
✦ collections of small items, especially ones that can be joined, such as centicubes, paper clips etc.
✦ a collection of money (1p, 2p, 5p and 10p)
✦ 0–9 number cards
✦ prepared sheets of paper with collections of dots to estimate and count

◆ Oral work and mental calculation

Counting forwards and backwards

✦ In preparation for the main activity, say *"You will be counting forwards and back in different ways and zero will not always be the starting point."* Prepare some cards with the numbers 1, 2, 5 and 10 written on them and have a large number line on display. Point to a number on the line, to indicate the start and hold up one of the number cards.

For example, point to 25 and hold up 5, to show they will count in 5s from 25. Go on to do a different count. Choose some children to write the finish number on the board.

◆ Starting point: whole class

✦ Tell the children that today they will be estimating, then counting, collections of things in different ways. Ask them to suggest ways of counting and write the first few examples on the board. Practise counting forwards and backwards in groups of 2, 5 and 10.
✦ Show your prepared sheets of dots and ask the children to estimate how many there might be and say how they would count to check.
✦ Show them a box containing a large number of interlocking cubes (at least 300). *"What would be the best way to find how many there are? Why do you think that way is best? Would you suggest the same method if there were fewer/more cubes?"* Record some estimates for the group 2 activity.

◆ Group activities

Focus group

Using the small items that can be joined together (paper clips, centicubes), ask the children to work in pairs to count their collection by grouping them in different ways, starting by counting in 10s. First they should write the number they think is in the collection, then count them, making a tally of the groups as they go along. Then ask them to repeat the counting but group them in a different way, for example grouping and counting in 5s. Ask, *"Is the answer still the same?"*

Teacher-independent groups

Group 1: Give this group some tiny plastic bags and collections of buttons or other small items. Ask them to work in pairs to find out how many there are. Suggest they count them into packs of ten to make the counting easier.

6
©Hopscotch Educational Publishing

developing
Numeracy
Skills

Numeracy
Year 3/P4

Counting and rounding

Group 2: Give this group the large collection of interlocking cubes you showed during the starter session, with the estimates they made. Ask them to work cooperatively to group the cubes to make counting easier. They should record the strategies they used and how close the estimates were.

Group 3: Give each pair of children a collection of money consisting of 1p, 2p, 5p and 10p coins. Ask them to count their collections and record what they did and how much money they had in their collections. Exchange collections within the group and check answers by comparing.

✦ Plenary session

✦ Discuss when the children might use different sorts of grouping for counting. Look at the number line and ask how many groups of 10 they would have in 100. Can they use their 0–9 cards to show this? Ask *"If there are 10 groups of 10 in 100, how many groups of 5 will there be?"* and *"When might people count in 100s or even 1000s?"*
✦ Ask Group 3 to explain their methods for counting the collections of money. Make the point that, when working with money, they can count it by grouping into 10s and 100s. *"What have you learned about estimating and counting?"*

✦ LESSON TWO NEARLY 10

✦ Assessment focus

Can the children understand rounding to the nearest 10?

✦ Resources

✦ collections of small items, such as cubes, counters and counting toys, in plastic bags or jars, measuring jugs, boxes
✦ 0–50 and 0–100 number lines
✦ coloured pens
✦ 0–9 cards or arrow cards

✦ Oral work and mental calculation

Place value

✦ Make a chart such as the one below on paper or use a commercial one.

10000	20000	30000	40000	50000	60000	to	90000
1000	2000	3000	4000	5000	6000	to	9000
100	200	300	400	500	600	to	900
10	20	30	40	50	60	to	90
1	2	3	4	5	6	to	9

✦ Talk to the children about the values of each number. Which are the larger/smaller values? Why? Discuss which of the numbers would be used to make 145, 4924 and so on. Write them on the board.
✦ Practise showing numbers using the 0–9 cards or arrow cards (taking care not to have repeats). Ask them to show you a number that is 10 more than 235, or 100 more than 671, and so on.

✦ Starting point: whole class

✦ Tell the children they will be working in groups of about four and that you want to find out how good they are at estimating. Explain that sometimes we do not need to know exactly how many things we have or how much they cost but it helps to know roughly how many there are. Discuss times when estimation might be useful. The ability to estimate is a valuable skill and children need to be taught the reason why it can be important.
✦ Show a small collection (about 14) of 2cm cubes in a bag and ask them, in their groups, to decide how many there are. Ask a child from each group to write their estimate on a large 1–100 number line at the front of the class, then to count the cubes and write the correct answer on the number line in a different colour.

Counting and rounding

◆ Talk about the way we move objects as we count them, but when we count drawings this is not possible. What could they do to make sure they do not count things twice? Perhaps they might use a pencil to draw round the pictures. Repeat this with other collections but using different objects and an increasing number of things each time. Can the children suggest when it is easiest to estimate almost exactly?

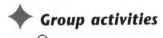

Group activities

 Focus group

Give each child a collection to be counted. Let them choose how to group but remind them about the way they grouped in the last lesson and assess the method used. When everyone has finished counting ask them to write the total on the number line. Discuss which of the multiples of 10 each total is nearest and explain that we call this 'rounding to the nearest 10' when we do not need to be absolutely accurate. Tell them that if the total ends in a 5, we usually round up to the next 10.

Teacher-independent groups

Activity sheet 1: Remind these children that they must find a way to check that they do not count something twice when they are counting the balloons. Suggest putting pencil lines around groups of balloons or ticking what has been counted.

Activity sheet 2: Give these children a variety of sizes of objects and a large measuring jug or box that will hold more than two handsful of the counting items.

Activity sheet 3: By giving the children small objects, like centicubes, and larger containers they will be using larger numbers for their estimates and the number lines they need to draw on will need to be extended beyond 100.

Plenary session

◆ Write some 2-digit and 3-digit numbers on the board. Ask, *"Can you round these numbers to the nearest 10?"*

◆ *"Although today you have been counting and rounding the numbers to the nearest 10, there are times when we can do this so that numbers are easier to add or subtract."* This gives an idea whether answers are sensible when we are using paper and pencil. *"So, 29 + 19 can be done as 30 + 20 = 50 and take off 2."*

◆ Use the numbers on the board to demonstrate how much easier it is to add in 10s. Write some 3-digit numbers on the board and round them to the nearest 100.

Further activities

◆ Working in groups of about four, ask the children to do some estimating and rounding. Give each group a bag containing a large number of cubes or counting toys – the collections must be the same for each group. At a word from you the children empty the bag on the table but must not touch the objects. Give them one minute to look at the collection and then as a group write an estimate of the number they think it contains. The estimates are written on the number line to the nearest 10. Repeat this with another collection.

Extension

◆ Give the children some pairs of numbers to add by rounding to the nearest 10 or 100, as appropriate, and then adjusting.

Support

◆ Give the children bags with small counting toys inside, keeping the numbers within their capabilities. It might help if they have some string 'circles' to count their groups of 10 into. Encourage them to count in 1s, 2s, 5s and 10s, helping them to learn the number sequences at the same time by counting out loud.

✦ Nearest to ... ✦

✦ Write under each set of balloons how many you think there are.
   You could use a pencil to group them so that they are easier to count.

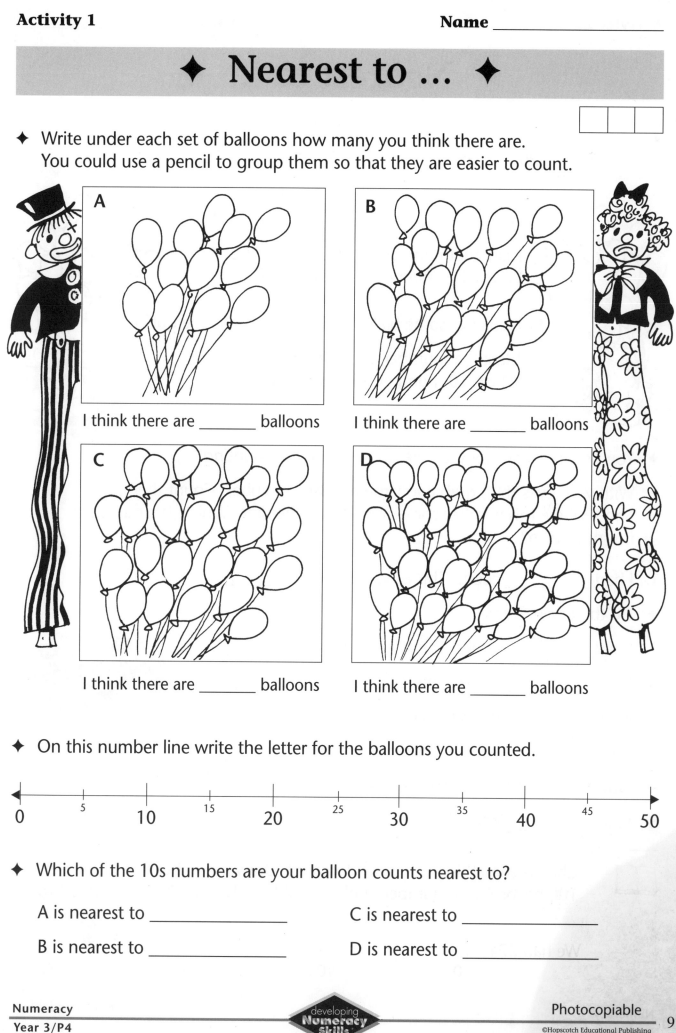

A

I think there are _____ balloons

B

I think there are _____ balloons

C

I think there are _____ balloons

D

I think there are _____ balloons

✦ On this number line write the letter for the balloons you counted.

0   5   10   15   20   25   30   35   40   45   50

✦ Which of the 10s numbers are your balloon counts nearest to?

A is nearest to _____   C is nearest to _____

B is nearest to _____   D is nearest to _____

Photocopiable
©Hopscotch Educational Publishing
9

✦ Nearest to ... ✦

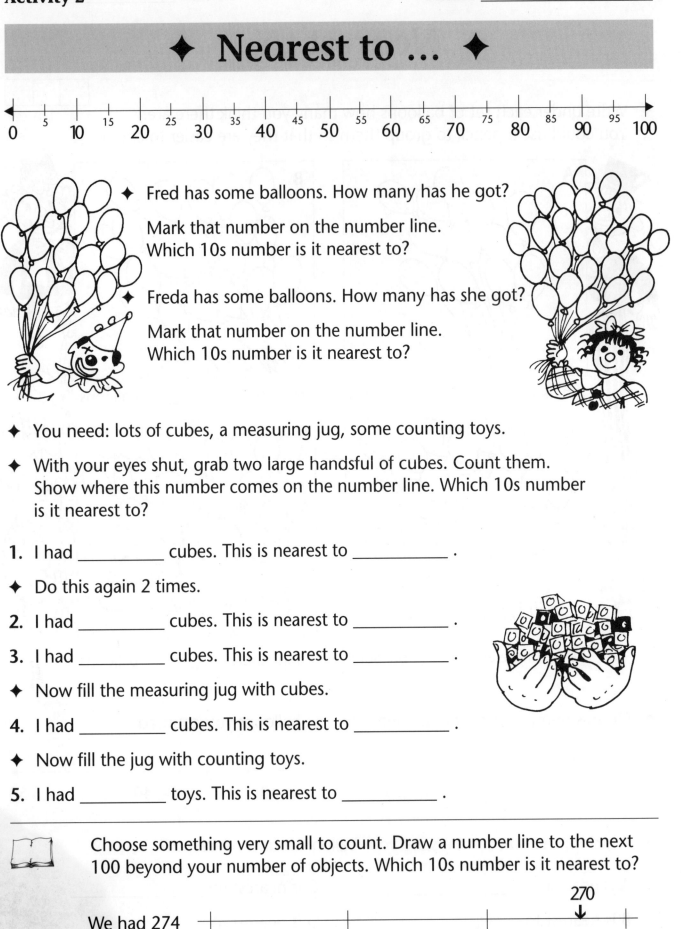

✦ Fred has some balloons. How many has he got?

Mark that number on the number line.
Which 10s number is it nearest to?

✦ Freda has some balloons. How many has she got?

Mark that number on the number line.
Which 10s number is it nearest to?

✦ You need: lots of cubes, a measuring jug, some counting toys.

✦ With your eyes shut, grab two large handsful of cubes. Count them.
Show where this number comes on the number line. Which 10s number
is it nearest to?

1. I had _____ cubes. This is nearest to _____ .

✦ Do this again 2 times.

2. I had _____ cubes. This is nearest to _____ .

3. I had _____ cubes. This is nearest to _____ .

✦ Now fill the measuring jug with cubes.

4. I had _____ cubes. This is nearest to _____ .

✦ Now fill the jug with counting toys.

5. I had _____ toys. This is nearest to _____ .

Choose something very small to count. Draw a number line to the next
100 beyond your number of objects. Which 10s number is it nearest to?

We had 274

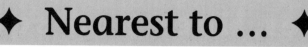

✦ Nearest to ... ✦

```
├────────────┼────────────┼────────────┼────────────┤
0           50           100          150          200
```

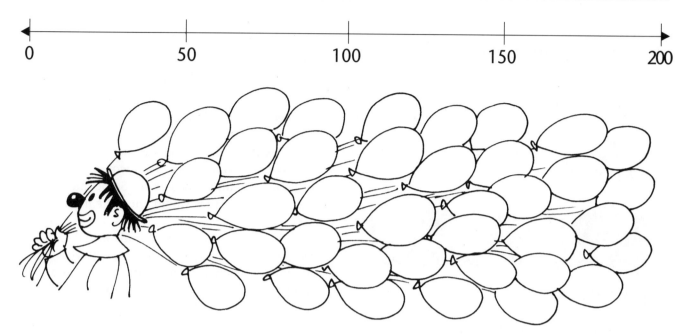

✦ How many balloons does Felix have? _____

✦ Mark that number on the number line.

✦ Which 10s number is it nearest to? _____

You need: centicubes and a box.

✦ With your eyes closed grab 2 handsful of centicubes. Count them and mark the number on the numberline. Which 10s number is it nearest to?

1. I had _____ cubes. This is nearest to _____ .

✦ Now use the box. Fill it with cubes. Count them and write which 10s number it is nearest to.

2. I had _____ cubes. This is nearest to _____ .

3. Try again with a larger container. In the space below, draw the number line you need to record your numbers on.

```
┌────────────────────────────────────────────────────┐
│                                                    │
│                                                    │
│                                                    │
│                                                    │
└────────────────────────────────────────────────────┘
```

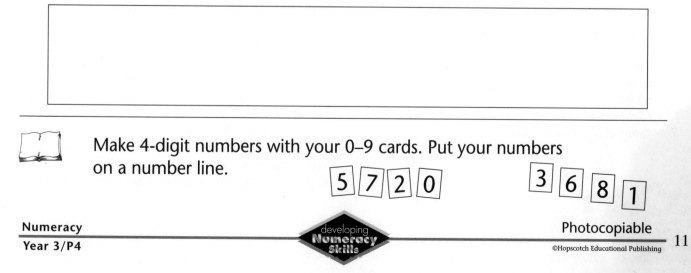

Make 4-digit numbers with your 0–9 cards. Put your numbers on a number line.

$\boxed{5}\boxed{7}\boxed{2}\boxed{0}$ $\boxed{3}\boxed{6}\boxed{8}\boxed{1}$

Number lines and squares

◆ Overall learning objectives

- ✦ Counting on and back in different-sized steps.
- ✦ Counting back beyond zero.
- ✦ Recognise odd and even numbers and use to make predictions.
- ✦ Recognise 2-digit multiples of 2, 5, 10 and 3-digit multiples of 100.

◆ LESSON ONE STEPPING OUT

◆ Assessment focus

Can the children describe and extend number sequences, including those extending beyond zero?

◆ Resources

- ✦ cubes/teddies
- ✦ blank number squares (see generic sheet 1 on page 90)
- ✦ 0–99 squares (see generic sheet 2 on page 91)
- ✦ number lines showing 0–30
- ✦ 0–10 number cards for each child
- ✦ coloured pens

◆ Oral work and mental calculation

Mixed mental calculations

- ✦ Display a 0–99 number square. Give questions that require quick answers based on the square, for example:
  "What is 30 more than 15?"
  "What is 70 less than 98?"
  "Start at 36, move down three squares and left 4 squares. What is the number? How many have you added?"
  "Subtract 17 from 93."
  "Start at 5 and take 3 steps of 3."

◆ Starting point: whole class

- ✦ Discuss odd and even numbers with the children. "Hamish, come and circle some even numbers on the number line. Now tell us why these are even." Could they recognise even numbers with two or more digits? How would they know this? "Jaswinder, tell us about the odd numbers." How would they recognise a multiple of 5 or 10? Some might be able to say how they would know the multiples of 100.
- ✦ Ensure everyone has a set of cards with 0, 2, 5, 10 written on them. Explain that you will write a number on the board and if they think it is a multiple of 2 they hold up the 2 card when you say "GO". Some of the numbers will be multiples of all three in which case they hold up 2, 5 and 10 but if the numbers you write are not multiples of these, they hold up 0.
- ✦ Blu-tack the number cards 0–20 into a set of odd and a set of even numbers to have on display for Group 1. Start the counting in 2s from 0 to get the group started.

◆ Group activities

Focus group

Give all the children a 0–99 square. Ask them to circle all the multiples of 10. "Are these odd or even? Now draw a square round all the multiples of 5." What can they say about the numbers with a square and circle? Next put a triangle round the multiples of 2. Which would be the next number after 100 to have a square, circle and triangle? Again, talk about the odd/even numbers. "If all the multiples of 4 were shaded, which would be the first number to also have the three shapes?" And the next?… How many between 0 and 100?… between 0 and 200? and so on.

Teacher-independent groups

Group 1: On a 0–30 number line ask the children to count in 2s starting with 0 and to mark the hops in red. What do they notice about the units digits? What would be the next number in the sequence? Repeat this, but starting from 1 and use a different

Number lines and squares

colour. If time allows they can add the numbers 21 to 30 to the display of odd and even numbers. What is the units sequence this time? Which are the odd and which the even numbers?

Group 2: Ask these children to make a 1–20 number strip on squared paper. When it is finished, tell them to cut it into pairs of numbers and add them, for example 1 + 2 = 3, and 3 + 4 = 7. They should then show the answer sequence on a number line.

Then make a 0–19 strip and repeat this. Encourage the children to work systematically and talk to them about the sequence of numbers. The aim is to enable them to generalise the fact that by adding an odd and an even number the answer is always odd, a fact that can be tested by using larger pairs of consecutive numbers, such as 37 + 38.

Group 3: Put a set of 0–9 cards in order, one on top of the other. Add the numbers systematically in pairs (0 + 1, 1 + 2 and so on). What do the children notice about the answers? Show the sequence as hops on a number line. Continue by adding the numbers in threes. What is the sequence this time? What if they add four numbers? Ask them to think carefully about adding odds and evens as they are working and to be ready to talk about what they have found out at the plenary session.

◆ Plenary session

◆ Ask someone from group 3 to write their first sequence on the board in full. *"Can anyone explain why an odd number plus an even number gives an odd answer? Does this always happen?"* Discuss some larger examples. Write up some of the generalisations the children make, for example *"When you add an odd and an even you get an odd number."*

◆ If you gave an answer could the children work out the two consecutive (next door) numbers they need to use? This can be done by halving, for example 15 + 16 = 31, so by halving the 30 they get the first number and so the second number must be 15 + 1.

◆ LESSON TWO — WHAT IS THE PATTERN?

◆ Assessment focus

Can the children give a sensible estimate and then check by counting?

◆ Resources

◆ 100 squares (see generic sheet 1 on page 90)
◆ number lines, including some with negative numbers, such as –20 to +20
◆ 0–9 cards

◆ Oral work and mental calculation

Addition and odds and evens

◆ Play a '5 minute circus race' game. Divide the class into two teams, the clowns and the jugglers. Set a timer for five minutes. As fast as they can, two of the clowns take a number card from a shuffled 0–9 pack and two of the jugglers throw a dice each. You write all four numbers on the board. All the children add them, call out the total and they also call out whether it is odd or even. If the total is odd, the clowns win a point and if it is even the jugglers win a point. At the end of five minutes count the scores. Is the winning score odd or even? Later in the year play the game using 10–20 cards (or higher) and dice with more than six faces.

Number lines and squares

✦ Starting point: whole class

✦ Write a simple number pattern on the board, such as 2, 4, 6, 8. Can the children talk about the pattern and predict how this would continue. Continue with a few more, including some with negative numbers, such as 7, 5, 3, 1, –1, –3 and show these on a number line. Tell them they will be looking for number patterns in their work, deciding how these will continue and writing what they notice about the patterns. Write up some of the children's comments about the patterns.

✦ *"Today you will be learning about number sequences and you will need to make some predictions about them."*

✦ Group activities

Focus group

Use –20 to +20 number lines. The children can work in pairs. Ask them to start at +20 and to hop back in 2s until they run out of line. Which number would be next if the line was extended? What if they started at +19? Would –45 be in the sequence? Why? What if they start at –17 and hopped on in 2s? Would +45 be in the sequence? Continue with hopping forward and back in groups of 3 and so on.

 Teacher-independent groups

Activity sheet 1: Explain that this worksheet has some numbers missing and they must work out how to fill them in.

Activity sheet 2: Ask these children to write the numbers where they belong on the number square and on the flags. You might decide to remove any that are visible in the classroom. Remind them that at the plenary session they will need to tell you about their patterns.

Activity sheet 3: This work is the same as for Group 2 but the numbers are larger.

✦ Plenary session

✦ Talk about the children's strategies for finding numbers in a sequence. What did they do to get clues? Who can explain the hardest sequence they did? Demonstrate numbers beyond 100 on a second number square. Ask for more predictions, *"If I count in 2s from 0, will I land on 25? How do you know?"*

✦ *"Let's all count back in 2s from zero."* Include some simple sequences for the least able.

✦ Further activities

✦ Give the children some cut-out sections from a blank number square, with some numbers filled in. Can the children fill in the missing numbers?

✦ Extension

✦ Give the children some small 0–99 squares. Ask them to colour every third number (the multiples of 3) and then describe the pattern made. What pattern do they get if all the multiples of 4 are coloured? Do either of the patterns have the same number coloured? For instance, 12 appears in both patterns.

✦ Support

✦ Draw a 6 x 6 number square on 2cm squared paper (or cut one from generic sheet 1 on page 90). Working in pairs, one child covers up some of the numbers and the other has to say which ones are covered. Ask them to explain what clues they used to help find the numbers.

1	2	3	4	5	6
7	8	9	10	11	12
13	14	15	16	17	18

✦ Where's my seat? ✦

✦ These are some seats at the circus. Write the missing numbers.

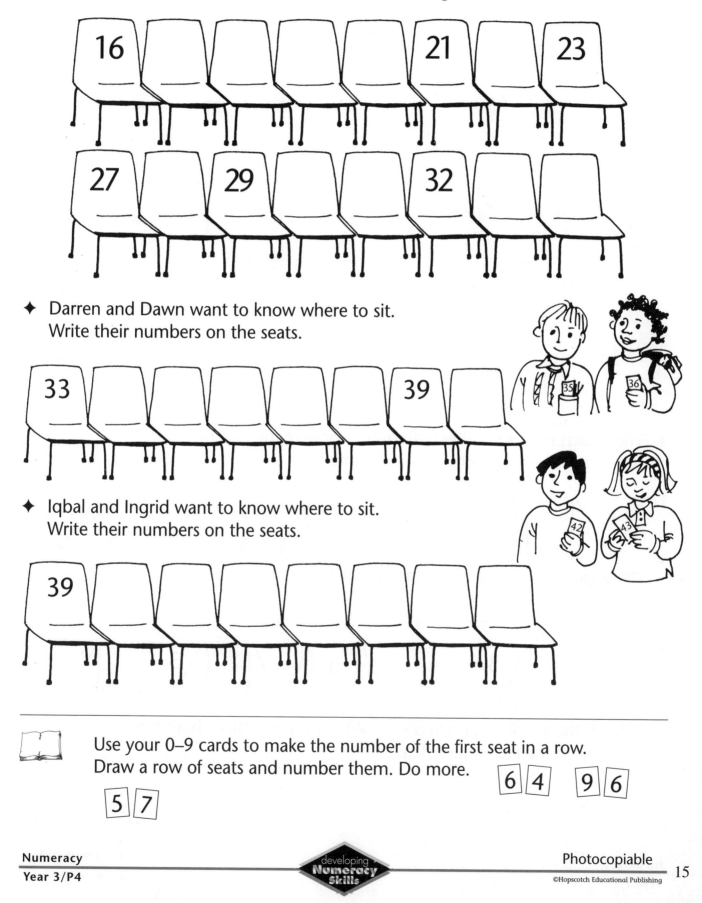

| 16 | | | | | 21 | | 23 |

| 27 | | 29 | | | 32 | | |

✦ Darren and Dawn want to know where to sit.
Write their numbers on the seats.

| 33 | | | | | | 39 | |

✦ Iqbal and Ingrid want to know where to sit.
Write their numbers on the seats.

| 39 | | | | | | | |

Use your 0–9 cards to make the number of the first seat in a row.
Draw a row of seats and number them. Do more.

6 4   9 6

5 7

Numeracy
Year 3/P4

developing
Numeracy
Skills

Photocopiable
©Hopscotch Educational Publishing

15

Name _____

✦ Where's my seat? ✦

✦ These tickets for the circus have the seat numbers on them. Write the numbers in the correct seats.

Rows of seats

1									
									100

✦ These flags have a number pattern but some of the numbers have washed off. Write the missing numbers.

1.

1   3   5   11

Write what you notice about the number pattern. _____

_____

2.

80   74   68

What is this number pattern doing?

_____

_____

developing **Numeracy Skills**

✦ Where's my seat? ✦

✦ These tickets for the circus have the seat numbers on them.
Write the numbers in the correct seats.

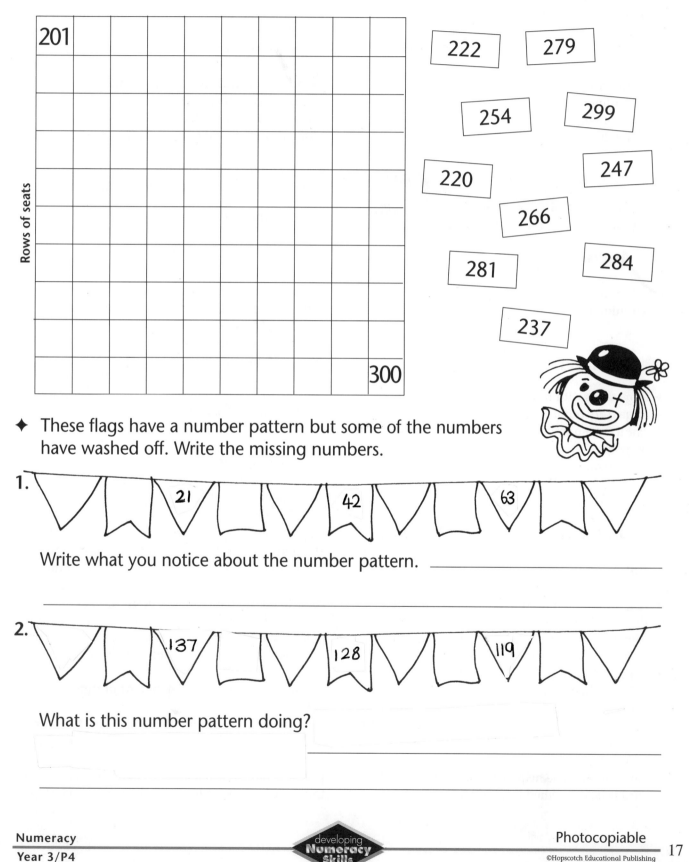

201									
									300

Rows of seats

222 279

254 299

220 247

266

281 284

237

✦ These flags have a number pattern but some of the numbers
have washed off. Write the missing numbers.

1. 21   42   63

Write what you notice about the number pattern. _____

_____

2. 137   128   119

What is this number pattern doing?

_____

_____

Place value

◆ Overall learning objectives

✦ Say numbers 1, 10, 100 or 1000 more than a given number.
✦ Add and subtract 1, 10, 100 or 1000 from any number.
✦ Compare and order numbers.
✦ Use ordinal language.
✦ Compare and order pairs of numbers and give mid-values.

LESSON ONE
MORE AND FEWER

◆ Assessment focus

Can the children add or subtract 1, 10 or 100 from a given number?

◆ Resources

✦ large cards with the numbers 1, 10, 100
✦ large 0–99 number square
✦ small 0–99 number squares (see generic sheet 2 on page 91)
✦ £1, 10p and 1p coins
✦ dice

◆ Oral work and mental calculation

Counting in 1s, 10s and 100s

✦ Ask the children to sit in a circle. Explain that they will be counting around in turn and that sometimes they will count on 1 more, sometimes 10 more and sometimes 100 more.
✦ Using the large cards with the numbers 1, 10 and 100, tell them that when you hold up one of these cards they change the number they will count on, so that the sequence might be: 0, 1, 2, 3, 4, 5 (hold up 10), 15, 25, 35, 45 (hold up 100), 145, 245, 345...
✦ Give the less able help by ensuring the 1 or 10 card is held up when it is their turn.

◆ Starting point: whole class

✦ Explain that the lesson will be about adding or subtracting multiples of 1, 10 or 100. Display the large 0–99 chart and use this to go over the patterns made by adding 1 or 10. Throw a dice and demonstrate the group 1 activity – you throw a 4, you add 10 people at the first bus stop, making 14, then another 10 and so on. Talk about what would happen as the people go home and you count back in 10s.
✦ Move on to 3-digit numbers. Show a grouping chart on the board and write a 3-digit number.

hundreds	tens	ones
2	6	5

✦ Ask the children to write the new numbers if any multiple of 1, 10 or 100 is added or subtracted, such as 265 + 100 = 365. Give several examples, asking them how they know what the new number is. Work towards them being able to talk about a rule. For example, *"When you add 40, you add 4 tens to the 10s column, but when you add hundreds you add the right number to the 100s column."*

◆ Group activities

 Focus group

Prepare some bags of money containing a selection of 10p and 1p coins. Explain that these bags of money are from the sales of sweets to the children during the interval at the circus. Can they reduce the number of coins to the smallest number possible? Can they explain what they did? Who had the largest amount of money? Can they combine the bags and work out a strategy for finding the total takings?

 Teacher-independent groups

Activity sheet 1: Remind this group how they can use a 0–99 square to add or subtract 10. Tell them that they are to throw a dice to find the number of people on the bus to go to the circus at the start and that 10 people want to get on the bus at each stop.

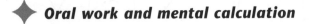

Place value

Activity sheet 2: Tell these children to think hard about the parts of the numbers that change as they add 1, 10 or 100 and which parts stay the same.

Activity sheet 3: Once the children have done a few examples on the sheet, ask them what they notice about the results. Ask them to write their generalisations to share later. How might they add 111 to a number? Change the machines to subtract 1, 10 or 100. Again, ask them to think about and write their generalisations about the rules for adding these numbers. How would they subtract 111? What if the machines changed to +2, +20, +200? (See Activity sheet 2 in Chapter 6.)

LESSON TWO
PUT THEM IN ORDER

◆ Assessment focus

Can the children order numbers up to 1000?

◆ Resources

◆ 0–99 square (see generic sheet 2 on page 91) with 'snakes' made from interlocking cubes or card
◆ 0–100 and 0–1000 number lines
◆ small sets of arrow cards, 0–9 and 10–90.
◆ large set of arrow cards, 0–9, 10–90 and 100–900.

◆ sets of 0–9 cards

◆ Oral work and mental calculation

Mixed mental calculations

◆ Give every child some 0–9 cards. Ask them to hold up the answers to add and subtract 1 or 10

◆ Plenary session

◆ Ask the children who did Activity sheet 1 to show what happens if the people on the bus get off 10 at a time when they go home. Can they explain how they worked? Ask a child from the other groups to describe their activity, what they found out and how this might help with mental work.
◆ *"Let's see if we can write the rule for adding 1, 10 or 100."* Write it up to keep for future reference.
◆ Write a number on the board and ask individuals to add/subtract 1, 10 or 100 and write the new number to keep a running total. After about ten children have had a turn, ask the class if they can go backwards through the list and say what happened each time, starting with the last number.

questions, followed by the addition of multiples of 10 to a given number. Put the questions in the context of the circus, for example *"16 people sat in the first row, 20 in the second. How many people?"*

◆ Starting point: whole class

◆ Put the large set of arrow cards face down on the table at the front of the class. Ask three children to come up, select a card from each set and make a 3-digit number to show to the class.
◆ Discuss the parts of numbers which are most significant when they are compared and ordered. *"Where would these numbers be put on a number line?"* Ask the children to write their numbers on a piece of paper and pin them to a 'washing line'. Repeat this with three more children. *"Where do their numbers fit on the line?"* Repeat once more.

◆ Group activities

Focus group

Tell the children they will be working in pairs with a set of arrow cards. They are to place the cards face down on the table and select a card each from the

Place value

ones pile. Ask them to write the two numbers on a section of number line with the smaller first. Can they write the number that falls halfway?

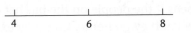

Discuss what happens if the difference between the two numbers is odd, for example:

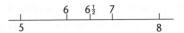

Repeat this with two of the 10s arrow cards, then with the 100s cards. What happens if they use 10s and 1s together? Investigate.

 Teacher-independent groups

Group 1: These children use a 0–99 square and a 'snake' made from five interlocking cubes. Working in pairs, one child places a 'snake' over some of the numbers and the other says which numbers are covered. If they are correct they score five points.

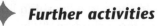

Extend this by using larger snakes or using a different arrangement of the numbers, such as on a 'Snakes and ladders' board, using generic sheet 1.

Group 2: Ask these children to work in pairs, each having a set of 0–9 cards placed face down on the table. They both turn over three cards which they use to make as many 1-, 2-and 3-digit numbers as possible. Can they mark on the 0–1000 number line where each of these numbers comes?

Group 3: Play nearest to 1000 (a game for two players). You need a board like the one below for each player and three of each of the numbers 0–9.

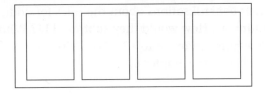

Shuffle the cards and place face down. Players take turns to take a card and put it on their game board with the aim of making a number as close to 1000 as possible. The player who is nearest is the winner. Play the 'nasty' version where a number can be put either on one's own board or the opponent's.

◆ Plenary session

◆ Ask the focus group to explain their strategies for finding midpoints, with an explanation on the board. Discuss what they might do with numbers greater than 100 or greater than 1000.

◆ *"Group 3, tell us about your strategies for winning both the nice and nasty versions of your game."*

◆ Further activities

◆ Play 'Place invaders' with a calculator. The children enter a 3-digit number into the calculator and they have to 'shoot down' first the 100s digit, then the 10s, followed by the 1s in one subtraction calculation. For example, 378 – 300 = 78, 78 – 70 = 8, 8 – 8 = 0. The numbers can be 'shot down' in a different order and the activity can be extended to include 4-digit numbers.

◆ Extension

◆ Using 2p, 5p and 10p coins, the children take turns to tell the others the total amount of money and the number of coins. *"I have made 49p with 7 coins."*

◆ Support

◆ Explore the use of calculator constants for 'add 1', 'add 10' and 'add 100' patterns.

◆ Counting in tens ◆

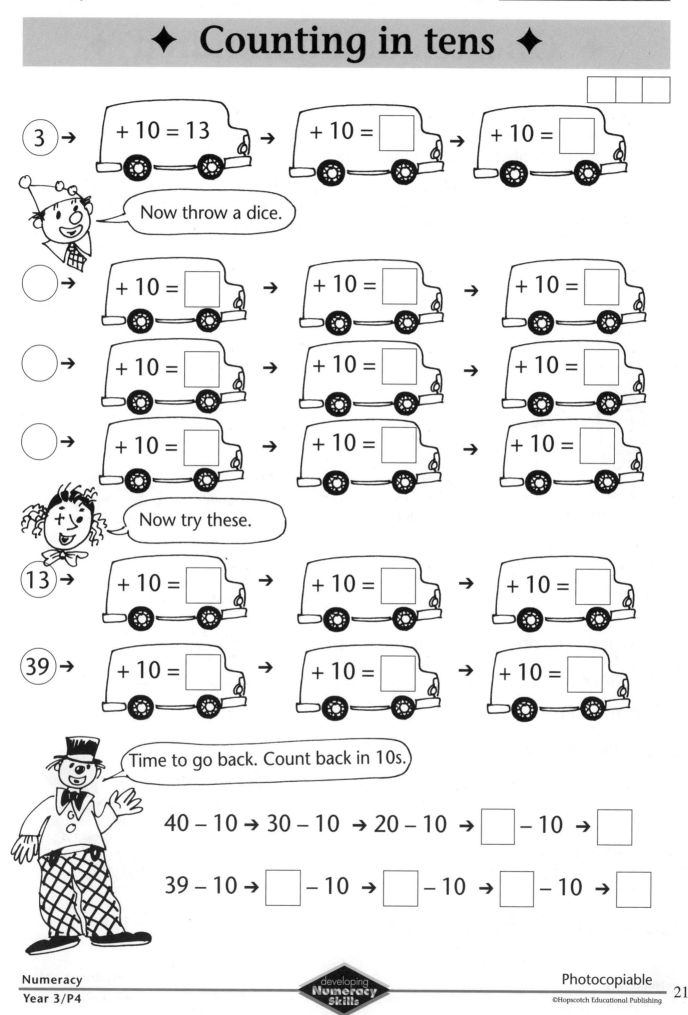

③ → + 10 = 13 → + 10 = ☐ → + 10 = ☐

Now throw a dice.

○ → + 10 = ☐ → + 10 = ☐ → + 10 = ☐

○ → + 10 = ☐ → + 10 = ☐ → + 10 = ☐

○ → + 10 = ☐ → + 10 = ☐ → + 10 = ☐

Now try these.

⑬ → + 10 = ☐ → + 10 = ☐ → + 10 = ☐

㊴ → + 10 = ☐ → + 10 = ☐ → + 10 = ☐

Time to go back. Count back in 10s.

$40 - 10 \rightarrow 30 - 10 \rightarrow 20 - 10 \rightarrow \boxed{} - 10 \rightarrow \boxed{}$

$39 - 10 \rightarrow \boxed{} - 10 \rightarrow \boxed{} - 10 \rightarrow \boxed{} - 10 \rightarrow \boxed{}$

Name _____

◆ One, ten and a hundred ◆

◆ Use a set of 0–9 cards to make a 2-digit number. Put the number into each machine in turn and write the new number. Do lots more. Look at the number patterns. One has been as an example.

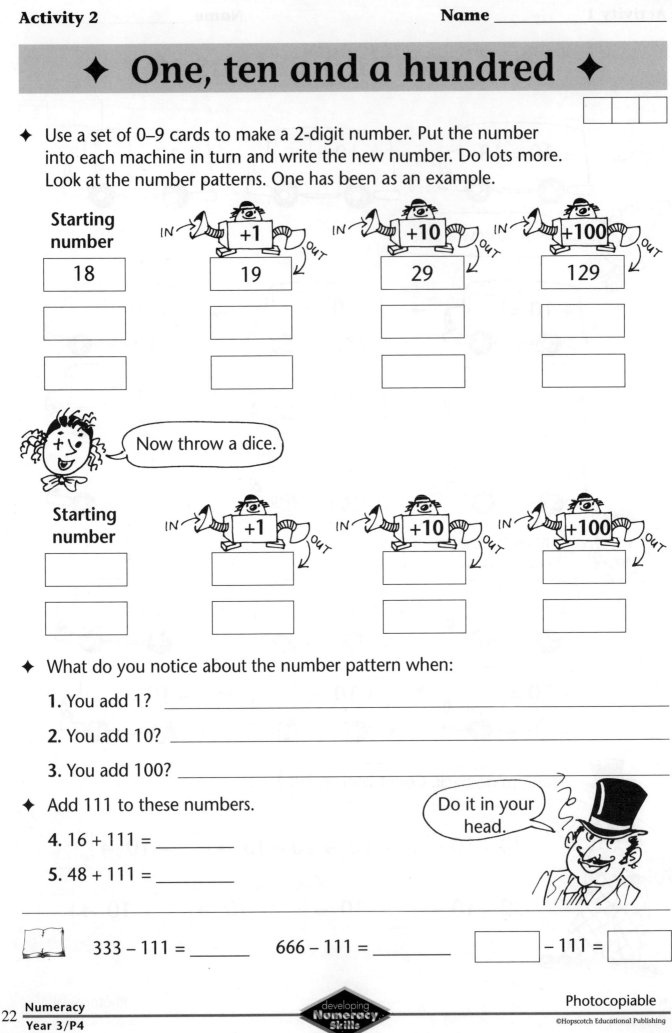

Starting number	IN +1 OUT	IN +10 OUT	IN +100 OUT
18	19	29	129

Now throw a dice.

Starting number	IN +1 OUT	IN +10 OUT	IN +100 OUT

◆ What do you notice about the number pattern when:

1. You add 1? _____

2. You add 10? _____

3. You add 100? _____

◆ Add 111 to these numbers.

Do it in your head.

4. 16 + 111 = _____

5. 48 + 111 = _____

333 − 111 = _____   666 − 111 = _____   ☐ − 111 = ☐

Photocopiable

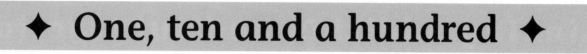

✦ One, ten and a hundred ✦

- ✦ You need a set of 0–9 cards. Shuffle them and turn them over facedown on the table. Turn over the top two and use the numbers to make a 2-digit number.
- ✦ Put the number into each machine in turn and write the new number. Do lots more. Look at the number patterns.

Starting number

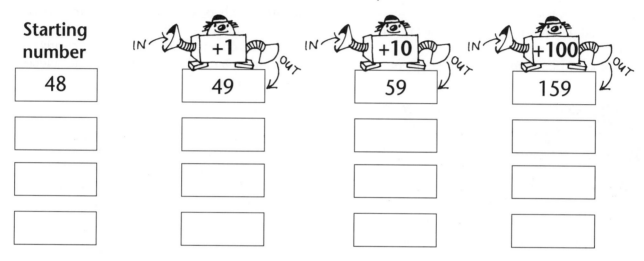

| 48 | 49 | 59 | 159 |

Starting number

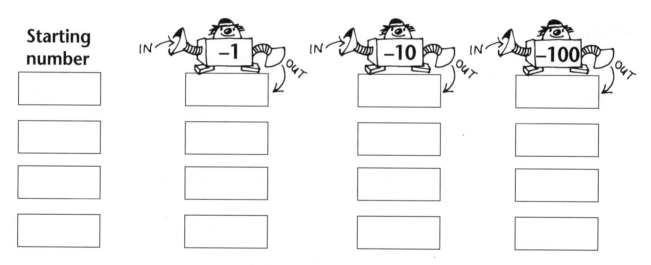

- ✦ What do you notice about the numbers when:

    1. You add 1? _____   **2.** You add 10? _____

    3. You add 100? _____   **4.** You subtract 1? _____

    5. You subtract 10? _____   **6.** You subtract 100? _____

📖 Choose some 3-digit numbers and find out what happens when you add 100.

Linking addition and subtraction

◆ Overall learning objectives

◆ Develop an understanding of addition and subtraction as inverse operations.
◆ Understand and use a range of vocabulary for addition and subtraction.
◆ Add more than two numbers mentally.
◆ Understand that numbers can be added in any order.
◆ Use symbols to stand for unknown numbers.

✦ LESSON ONE
THERE AND BACK AGAIN ✦

◆ Assessment focus

Can the children understand and use the relationship between addition and subtraction?

◆ Resources

◆ number lines with multiples of 10
◆ cubes
◆ cards numbered 1–10
◆ cards numbered 1–20
◆ 0–9 dice and a dice marked 0, 0, 10, 10, 100, 100.

◆ Oral work and mental calculation

Adding and subtracting multiples of 5, 10 and 100

◆ Draw a number line on the board showing the multiples of 10. Remind the children how these can be used for adding and subtracting, then practise some examples, such as 30 + 20 and 90 – 40, asking some children to demonstrate how they might do it using steps of 10. *"Lucy, how would you work out 25 + 40? What about 15 + 25?"*
◆ Change the number line to 100–900 and continue to do this by adding and subtracting in 100s, then in 50s.

◆ Starting point: whole class

◆ Write a simple number fact on the board, such as 10 + 5 = 15, and invite children to show another way of writing this as addition, without splitting numbers (5 + 10 = 15). Then go on to show how the three numbers can be changed around to show 15 – 10 = 5 and 15 – 5 = 10. Demonstrate these calculations on a number line, showing clearly how jumping back along the number line 'undoes' the jumping forward.

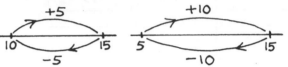

◆ Write a harder example on the board and invite a child show to how this might be done on the number line, reminding them that if they can remember one number fact they can use it to work out three others. For example:

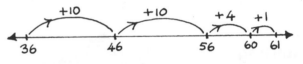

$$36 + 25 = 61$$

The number line can then be used to show:
$$61 - 25 = 36$$
$$25 + 36 = 61$$
$$61 - 36 = 25$$

◆ *"You don't have to jump along the number line in 10s, you could jump on 20 instead of two 10s."*

◆ Group activities

 Focus group

Prepare an addition square to suit the abilities of the group:

+	5	4	3	2	1
6					
7			10		
8					
9	14				
10					

or

+	21	25			
10				37	40
15	36				
			50		
			55		
35					65

Linking addition and subtraction

Ask the children how they will fill in the missing numbers. Once they have filled in all the spaces, give some written addition calculations, using the words 'plus', and 'equals'. These can be written on the board for the plenary session. Discuss how the square could be used for subtraction and once the children have got the idea, select three of the numbers and ask them to write as many sentences as they can using addition and subtraction.

 Teacher-independent groups

Activity sheet 1: The number lines on this sheet have been kept very simple. At the plenary session you could ask this group to explain how hopping forward is undone by hopping back. For question 3, either you or the child can select the numbers.

Activity sheet 2: These children must find one addition fact using three numbers and use this to find another three addition or subtraction facts.

Challenge them to use demanding 2-digit numbers for the maths book challenge.

Activity sheet 3: This sheet extends the work for this group because the numbers are more demanding. Encourage them to work mentally. The maths book task can be done without numbers, for example:

✦ *Plenary session*

✦ Invite the focus group to talk about the different words we use to make number sentences, for example '17 minus 3 is 14' and display these for use during mental maths time. Ask the children who did activity sheet 1 to demonstrate their number line hops. *"So what does subtraction do to addition?"*

✦ *"Tell me some things you know about addition and subtraction."*

✦ ✦ ✦ ✦ ✦ ✦   ✦ ✦ ✦ ✦ ✦ ✦

✦ LESSON TWO ✦ WHICH WAY ROUND?

✦ *Assessment focus*

Can the children understand that addition can be done in any order and use a range of mathematical vocabulary to describe their work?

✦ *Oral work and mental calculation*

Understanding equations

✦ Write an equation on the board, such as $10 = \Box + 7$. Talk about the possible numbers for $\Box$ and that = means 'balances' (so both sides of the = sign must balance). Give a few more examples, such as $\Box + \Box = 20$. The children should then work in pairs to talk about $\Box + 10 = \Box + \Box$. (There is an infinite number of options!)

✦ Later in the year do $\triangle + \Box = \bigcirc$ as above.
✦ Write all the number sentences you can make with 2, 8 and 10, for example $2 + 8 = 10$ and $10 - 2 = 8$ and $10 - 8 = 2$.

✦ *Starting point: whole class*

✦ Revise adding pairs of numbers that total multiples of 10, for example:

✦ Write several numbers on the board and ask the children what they think will be a good way to add them. Can they show the others their method on the board? Are the answers different if they are done in a different order?

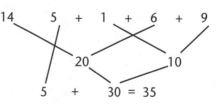

Linking addition and subtraction

✦ *"Today we will be using what we know about numbers that add to 10 or 20 and so on to help us add several numbers together."* Work with some examples together, such as 46 + 14 + 7 + 13 and 4 + 51 + 6 + 9.

✦ Repeat the calculations by writing the numbers in a different order. Use some examples where three numbers total 10, such as 1 + 12 + 6 + 3 + 8.

✦ Demonstrate the group 1 game.

◆ Group activities

Focus group

On some large sheets of paper write about four or five 2-digit numbers that can be added to make multiples of 10, such as 34 + 45 + 15 + 16. Ask the children to work in pairs and decide how they are going to add the numbers, using the method used in the starting activity. Tell them that once they have done that they can write the numbers in a different order and try a different method. Talk with them about the ways of adding the numbers and discuss which method is most helpful, so that they can explain it to the others at the plenary session.

Teacher–independent groups

Group 1: These children need a set of 1–9 cards. These are shuffled and placed face down on the table. Five numbers are turned over. Say that the numbers can be written down in any order but the children need to look for pairs or groups of numbers that add up to 10 just as you have been showing on the board. Tell them to arrange the numbers in a different order and add them again. Are the answers the same? Shuffle the cards again and repeat.

Group 2: These children should do the same as group 1, but using cards numbered 1–20.

Group 3: This group can work in pairs. They will need one 0–9 dice and one dice marked 0, 0, 10, 10, 100, 100 for each pair. The two dice are thrown and the two numbers added to make 1-, 2- or 3-digit numbers. The dice need to be thrown four or five times to make the numbers for them to work with.

◆ Plenary session

✦ Ask one person from each group, including the focus group to explain one example from their work to the others. Talk about the method of putting numbers together to make 10s and how useful it is.

✦ Do a brief introduction for the next lesson by writing two numbers on the board and say that tomorrow they will use subtraction. *"Does it matter which order the numbers are written in?"* (Yes!) Ask the children to suggest what happens. *"What happens if the smaller number is written first?"* When doing subtraction the order is important, unlike addition and in the case of putting a smaller number first the answer will be negative.

◆ Further activities

✦ Do some 'dartboard' activities. Explore the different totals that can be made with three (or more) 'throws'.

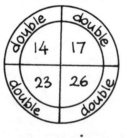

✦ Play 'Snap'. The numbers to be 'snapped' must add to 10.

✦ Play 'Triominoes' using generic sheets 3 and 4 (pages 92 and 93).

◆ Extension

✦ *"Red cubes cost 5p, green cost 10p and blue cost 20p. Make a robot costing £5. Can a robot be made using as few/many cubes as possible? How many different robots could be made?"*

◆ Support

✦ Throw a 1–6 dice several times and make 'sticks' with linking cubes in a single colour for each number. Put all the 'sticks' together and count the cubes. Rearrange and count again.

✦ There and back again ✦

1.

+7

3   10

−7

$3 \ + \ 7 \ = \ 10$

$7 \ + \ \boxed{} \ = \ 10$

$10 \ - \ 7 \ = \ \boxed{}$

$10 \ - \ 3 \ = \ \boxed{}$

Draw an 'add 10' jump on the number line, then jump back again.

2.

+10

2

$2 \ + \ 10 \ = \ \boxed{}$

$10 \ + \ 2 \ = \ \boxed{}$

$12 \ - \ \boxed{} \ = \ \boxed{}$

$12 \ - \ \boxed{} \ = \ \boxed{}$

Now use these 3 numbers.

$\boxed{} \ \boxed{}$ and $\boxed{}$

3.

$\boxed{} \ + \ \boxed{} \ = \ \boxed{}$

$\boxed{} \ + \ \boxed{} \ = \ \boxed{}$

$\boxed{} \ + \ \boxed{} \ = \ \boxed{}$

$\boxed{} \ + \ \boxed{} \ = \ \boxed{}$

Use your number cards to make more additions.

$\boxed{9} \ \boxed{3} \ \boxed{2}$ $\boxed{} \ + \ \boxed{} \ = \ \boxed{}$

◆ There and back again ◆

Draw the jumps you need to make on a number line to find your answers.

If you know 16 + 13 = 29, you know more facts

1. 16 + 13

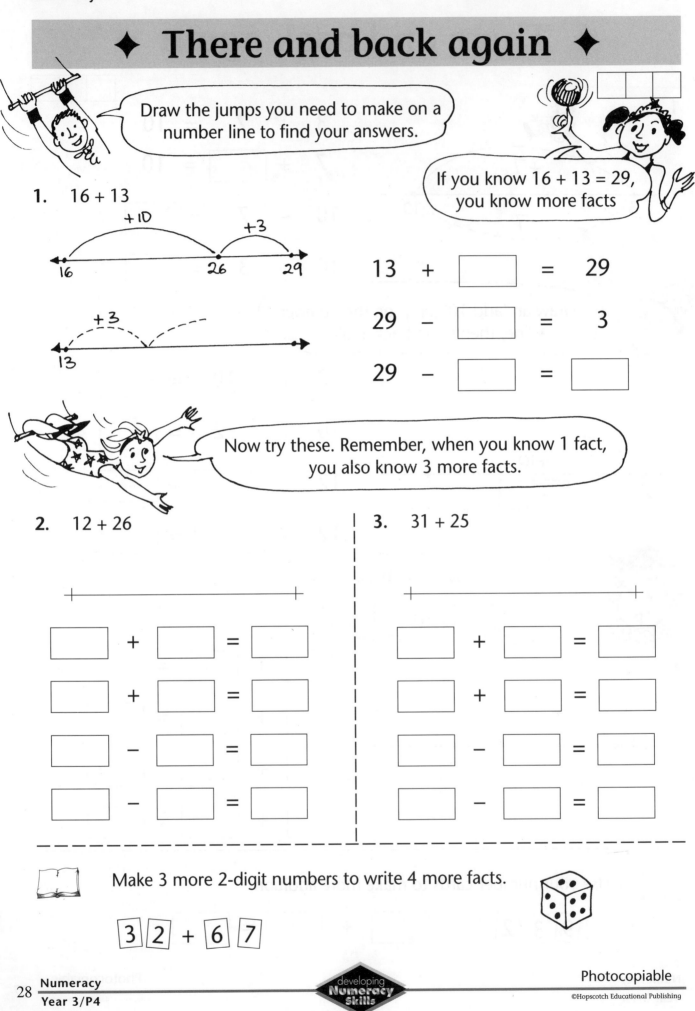

13 + ▢ = 29

29 – ▢ = 3

29 – ▢ = ▢

Now try these. Remember, when you know 1 fact, you also know 3 more facts.

2. 12 + 26

▢ + ▢ = ▢

▢ + ▢ = ▢

▢ – ▢ = ▢

▢ – ▢ = ▢

3. 31 + 25

▢ + ▢ = ▢

▢ + ▢ = ▢

▢ – ▢ = ▢

▢ – ▢ = ▢

- -

Make 3 more 2-digit numbers to write 4 more facts.

3 2 + 6 7

◆ There and back again ◆

Find the answer to the first calculation. Check by using the numbers in a different order.

1.   35   +   44   =   [ ]   **2.**   67   +   28   =   [ ]

Check   **Check**

44   +   35   =   [ ]   28   +   67   =   [ ]

Use subtraction   **Use subtraction**

[ ]   –   44   =   [ ]   [ ]   –   28   =   [ ]

[ ]   –   [ ]   =   [ ]   [ ]   –   [ ]   =   [ ]

---

3. Write 4 facts with these numbers.

14   42   28

_____   _____

_____   _____

4. Write 4 facts with these numbers.

46   19   65

_____   _____

_____   _____

Choose 3 numbers and write number sentences using these words.

altogether makes	plus	minus
	equals	

_____

_____

_____

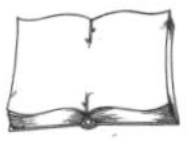

If you know [ ] + △ = ○

write 3 more facts.

If you use numbers it might help.

Mental calculation strategies

◆ Overall learning objectives

◆ Understand that addition can be done in any order.
◆ Identifying doubles and/or near doubles.
◆ Adding pairs of numbers that cross the 10s boundary.
◆ Partition and recombine numbers.
◆ Explain mental methods using a range of mathematical vocabulary.

◆ LESSON ONE ◆
TURN IT ROUND

◆ Assessment focus

Can the children use the strategy of putting the larger number first?

◆ Resources

◆ 100 squares (use generic sheet 1 on page 90 and fill in the numbers)
◆ dice marked 1, 1, 2, 2, 3, 3
◆ 0–9 cards
◆ cards with multiples of 10 – 100.

◆ Oral work and mental calculation

Number bonds of 10, 20 and above

◆ Play 'Complements', starting with complements of 10, where you hold up a card with a number, such as 6, and the children have to hold up the card that makes 10 (4) as quickly as they can. After a while change to complements of 20 and encourage the children to recall the facts as quickly as possible. You can continue with complements of the multiples of 10 up to 100 and progress to the multiples of 5, for example 35 + 65 = 100. Ask some of the children to explain their methods for working out the complements.

◆ Starting point: whole class

◆ Write the calculation 14 + 58 on the board. Use the 100 square to show the children how this can be done by starting on the 14, counting 50 down in 10s and then counting on 8 more (or alternatively, 6 more to get to 70 and then counting on the remaining 2). This example shows that by starting with 14, the 58 had to be partitioned into 5 tens, a 6 to bring 64 up to 70 and then the remaining 2 had to be added. Ask the children if this could have been done a different way. Accept any suggestions that the 58 could have been partitioned differently, such as 2 twenties, 10, 6 and 2. If no one suggests putting the larger number first, ask if this could be done and then invite one of the children to show on the number square how much easier this would be.
◆ Try another example, again putting a smaller number first, such as 7 + 64. Demonstrate this on a number line and leave it on display for group 1 to use. Show them how they can generate their own numbers with dice and cards for group work.

◆ Group activities

Focus group

Start by asking the children to turn over two of their 0–9 cards to make a 2-digit number. One more card is turned over and added mentally to the 2-digit number. Ask for any strategies the children have used. Continue by making 3-digit numbers and adding first a 1-digit, progressing to 2-digit numbers.

Teacher-independent groups

Group 1: Give these children two 1, 1, 2, 2, 3, 3 dice. Explain that they are to throw the dice to make a 2-digit number. They then repeat this to make a second 2-digit number, then add the two numbers, putting the larger one first. Can they show what they did on a number line or 100 square?

Group 2: This group should use their sets of 0–9 cards to create two 2-digit numbers and find the

Mental calculation strategies

totals by putting the larger number first. Encourage them to talk about how they might do this using their 100 squares.

Group 3: Ask these children to use 1–9 cards and give them a set of cards with the multiples of 10–100 written on them. They make a 2-digit number using their 1–9 cards and then turn over a multiple of 10 card. The two numbers are added, putting the larger number first. Once the children are working confidently ask them to make 3-digit numbers with their cards and add a multiple of 10.

◆ *Plenary session*

◆ *"Why does it help to put the larger number first? In what situations is it most helpful?"* If the numbers are fairly close together would a different strategy be better? Ask one person from each group to explain to the class how they worked.
◆ Conclude by playing a game of 'Back to back' where two children stand back to back and are given an addition calculation, such as 6 + 184. The first to answer chooses another child to stand back to back and another calculation is given.

LESSON TWO
USING THE NUMBER LINE

◆ *Assessment focus*

Can the children explain their strategies for addition and subtraction using the number line?

◆ *Resources*

◆ blank number lines
◆ linking cubes
◆ arrow cards

◆ *Oral work and mental calculation*

Doubling and halving

◆ Shuffle a pack of 1–50 cards. Show the top card and write it on the board. *"Who can tell me the number that is the double of this number?"* *"Stephan, come and write the answer underneath the first number."* Next ask them to double the answer and ask a volunteer to write it under the last double. Repeat this, asking the children to explain how they doubled the larger numbers. Relate doubling to the 2x table. Later in the year do halves of numbers as well.

◆ Choose another number and repeat. The children can be asked to show their answers using either arrow cards or 0–9 cards.

◆ *Starting point: whole class*

◆ Write a calculation on the board, such as 26 + 37. Explain how this might be done using jumps.

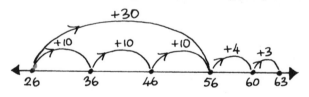

◆ Show them that they could group their +10s together to make +30. Explain that an alternative strategy could have been:

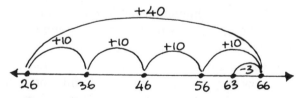

◆ This shows that it is possible to count on to the next multiple of 10 and subtract the difference. Remind them that if they wanted to, they could change the calculation to 37 + 26. Invite them to suggest ways of using the number line for adding pairs of numbers. Then move on to subtraction.

©Hopscotch Educational Publishing

Mental calculation strategies

◆ Group activities

Focus group

Start with an empty number line and a pair of numbers to be added written on a large sheet of paper. Ask the children to suggest a method for doing the addition by partitioning the number to be added. Help them to count on in 10s using their number lines or, if necessary, model the jumps using interlocking cubes. Give the children some large pieces of paper with empty number lines and two numbers to add together. Ask them to work in pairs and to discuss how to find the answers.

Teacher-independent groups

Activity sheet 1: This sheet gives the children some 2-digit numbers to add, showing the jumps they make on a number line as a lead-in to developing paper and pencil methods from mental strategies. Explain that you would also like them to write the separate numbers they added to get their answers. Only addition is used in the main activity. The continuation activity asks them to make two 2-digit numbers and to subtract them, again showing the jumps. Some of the questions just bridge through to the next multiple of 10.

Activity sheet 2: This includes bridging to the next 10 and using 3-digit numbers and the last calculation is a subtraction. The continuation activity involves making a 2-digit and a 3-digit number, adding them using the number line and then subtracting the same pair of numbers.

Activity sheet 3: This sheet provides more challenging opportunities to work on addition with 3-digit numbers. They continue by subtracting 2-digit, beginning to bridge back across the multiples of 10.

◆ Plenary session

- ◆ Ask the focus group to show their work to the class, with one of the pairs choosing an example to explain what they did. Ask group 2 to demonstrate on the board some of their strategies for adding larger numbers, encouraging them to show the individual jumps of 10 and also how these could be grouped, if appropriate into larger multiples of 10.
- ◆ Invite group 3 to explain how they worked on bridging the multiples of 100. Continue to demonstrate how the work they have been doing can be extended to larger numbers.

◆ Further activities

- ◆ Teach the children to check calculations by using the inverse operation. For example, if 79 – 13 is 66, then 66 + 13 should be 79.
- ◆ Give mental calculations showing children how they can make informal jottings on scrap paper in order to move towards more formal recordings.

◆ Extension

- ◆ Develop the continuation on Activity sheet 3 and give the children experience of larger numbers.

◆ Support

- ◆ Children who are struggling will need more experience with + and – of 2-digit numbers. Work towards them being able to do Activity sheet 2.

✦ Along the lines ✦

✦ Show all your jumps along the number lines.

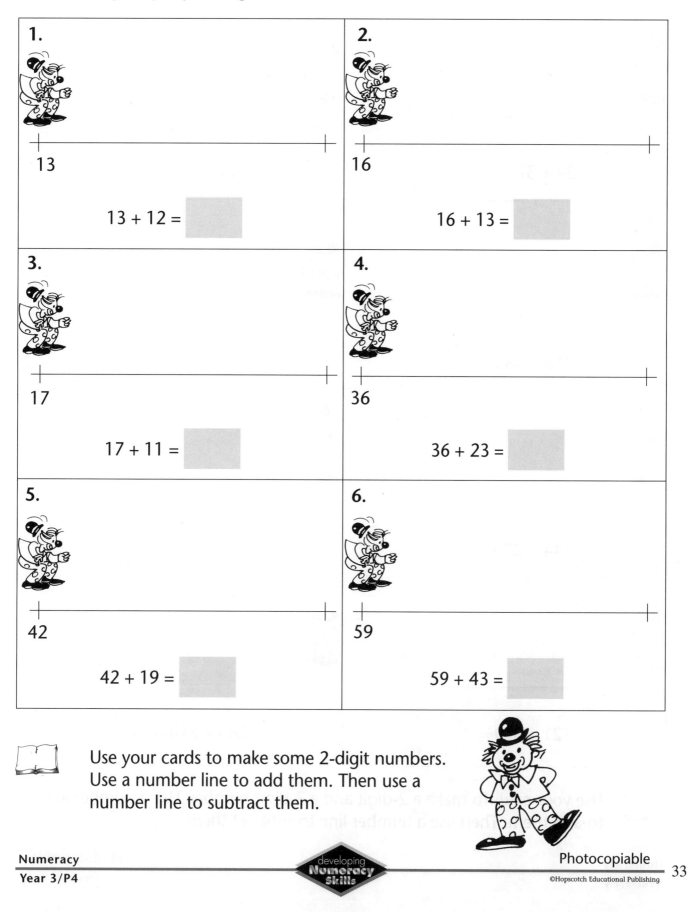

1.

13

13 + 12 =

2.

16

16 + 13 =

3.

17

17 + 11 =

4.

36

36 + 23 =

5.

42

42 + 19 =

6.

59

59 + 43 =

Use your cards to make some 2-digit numbers. Use a number line to add them. Then use a number line to subtract them.

✦ Along the lines ✦

✦ Show your number line jumps.

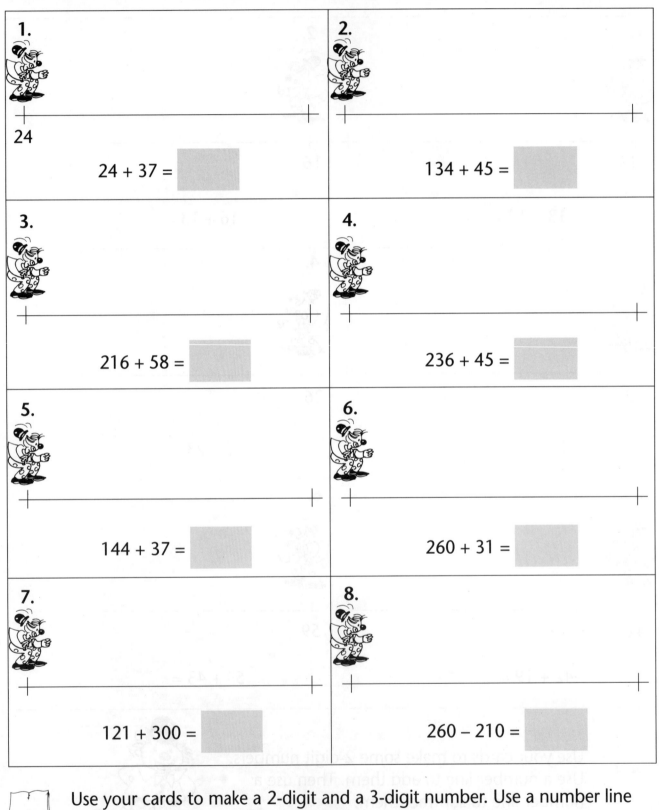

1.

24

24 + 37 =

2.

134 + 45 =

3.

216 + 58 =

4.

236 + 45 =

5.

144 + 37 =

6.

260 + 31 =

7.

121 + 300 =

8.

260 – 210 =

Use your cards to make a 2-digit and a 3-digit number. Use a number line to add them. Then use a number line to subtract them.

Photocopiable
©Hopscotch Educational Publishing

developing **Numeracy Skills**

✦ Along the lines ✦

✦ Show two different number line jumps for each calculation.

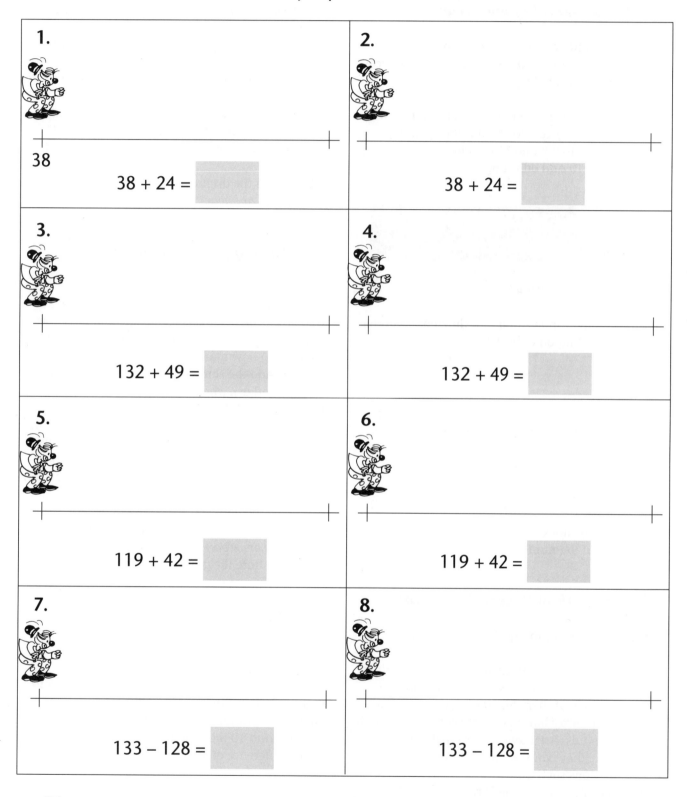

1.

38

$38 + 24 =$

2.

$38 + 24 =$

3.

$132 + 49 =$

4.

$132 + 49 =$

5.

$119 + 42 =$

6.

$119 + 42 =$

7.

$133 - 128 =$

8.

$133 - 128 =$

Use your cards to make a 2-digit and a 3-digit number. Show three different ways of adding your two numbers on a number line.

Counting and estimating

◆ Overall learning objectives

◆ Find small differences by counting on or back.
◆ Count on or back in 10s and 1s to find differences.
◆ Develop the vocabulary for explaining about differences.
◆ Use the number line to find pairs of numbers with the same difference and explain their findings.
◆ Add and subtract 9 and 11 by adding or subtracting 10 and adjusting.

◆ LESSON ONE HOW MANY?

◆ Assessment focus

Can the children understand that differences can be found by counting on or back?

◆ Resources

◆ number lines, including 0–20 and a matching number strip 0–5
◆ 100 squares
◆ money
◆ dice
◆ metre rules
◆ interlocking cubes
◆ a display of the numbers 1–9 as in a calculator

◆ Oral work and mental calculation

Developing mental images

◆ Display the 1–9 arrangement of numbers as they appear on a calculator's keys. Tell the children they can look at them for 10 seconds, then you will turn it away but they must keep a picture of it in their minds. Ask them to close their eyes to make sure they can see it in their minds.
◆ Ask questions such as:
"Which number is in the middle?"
"Which number is on the top right?" and *"Bottom left?"*

"Which pattern of numbers is down the right side? Which number would come next?"
"What is the difference between the number at the middle left and the bottom left?"
"What is the difference between the number at the top right and the bottom left?"
"What do the numbers in the first row total?" and *"The sum of the second row? and the third row?"*
"If there was another row of numbers what would they total?"
◆ Each time the display can be turned round to check the answers.

◆ Starting point: whole class

◆ Demonstrate simple differences with two towers of cubes or large bricks. Ask what the difference is between the heights of them – how many cubes is this? Explain that we can find the difference by counting how many more/fewer cubes in each tower. Add the same number of cubes to each tower and ask what the difference is now.
◆ Place the numbers 0–30 in a line on the floor so all the children can see. Ask two of them to stand on a number each and discuss how many must be counted to get from the first to the second. How many more/less is that? If both children move one space to the right, what is the difference now? What if they move three spaces to the left, what is the difference? *"Differences can be found by counting on or back."*
◆ Demonstrate the group 1 activity.

◆ Group activities

 Focus group

These children need two dice, which they throw to make a 2-digit number. This is the start number. They use a number line to find the numbers that are 10 fewer and 10 more, so they have three numbers with a difference of 10.

36
©Hopscotch Educational Publishing

developing
Numeracy
Skills

Numeracy
Year 3/P4

Counting and estimating

Teacher-independent groups

Group 1: Give these children a 0–20 number line with the numbers 1cm apart. Tell them they are going to use it to find pairs of numbers with a difference of 5. Ask them to cut a strip of paper the same length as 0–5 on the number line and show them how they can place one end, for example, on the 5 and that the number at the other end of their paper strip is 10. This means that the numbers 5 and 10 have a difference of 5. By placing one end of the strip on a different number and reading off the number at the other end they will have another pair of numbers with a difference of 5.

Group 2: Each pair of children needs a set of 0–9 cards placed face down. They both turn over two cards and make two 2-digit numbers as close to each other as possible. Using a 0–99 square they calculate the difference between the numbers by counting on and by counting back to compare the answers.

Group 3: This group should find the difference in amounts of money. They work in pairs using a mixed collection of coins, including 50p pieces. Ask them to choose three coins each and calculate how much they each have. They compare the amounts and work out how much more or less money one has than the other. They could record this as a table.

Fred's money	Mary's money	Difference

✦ Plenary session

✦ Ask some of the children to explain to the class how they found differences. Group 3 could explain how they found differences in money. Did they use counting on or back? Were there times when they used facts they knew? Was there anything in the lesson that was new?

✦ ✦ ✦ ✦ ✦ ✦

✦ LESSON TWO ✦ SUBTRACTING 9 and 11

✦ Assessment focus

Can the children use their knowledge of subtracting 10 to subtract 9 and 11?

✦ Resources

✦ 1–100 number cards and number lines
✦ cubes
✦ dice

✦ Oral work and mental calculation

Approximating with addition and subtraction

✦ Write these six numbers on the board: 191, 92, 63, 139, 109, 159. Ask the children to work in small groups to find pairs of numbers that add up

to almost 250. (191 + 63 = 254, 92 + 159 = 251, 139 + 109 = 248) *"How did you work that out?"*
✦ Focus on approximating. *"191 is almost 200 and 63 is about 60, so 200 + 60 is close to 250."*
✦ *"Now find 2 numbers with a difference of about 50."* (159 – 109).
✦ *"How do I know the difference between 109 and 151 isn't about 50?"*

✦ Starting point: whole class

✦ Ask the children to arrange individual numbers 1–100 to make a large 100 square on the floor. Remind them how we use the square to add multiples of 10 to any number on the square. Ask a child to demonstrate 45 + 10 by putting a red cube on 45 and 55. Ask another child to start at 45 and count on 9 more, putting a yellow cube on the answer. A third child could put a blue cube on the number that is 11 more than 45. Try some more examples, including 37 + 20, 37 + 19 and 37 + 21. Work on the subtraction of 9, 10 and 11.

Counting and estimating

◆ This can also be demonstrated on a number line which is just like a 100 square that is stretched out. Demonstrate jumps of 10, 9 and 11. 13 + 9 can be found by counting on 10 and then counting back 1.

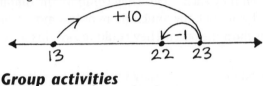

◆ Group activities

Focus group

Ask the children to make a line of cubes that is 10 long. They throw a dice and write the number, then make a line with that number of cubes. What number does it make if they add the 10 cubes? Can they show that on a number line? Can they tell you what number it would make if they had added only 9, or if 11 had been added? Repeat several times.

Teacher-independent groups

Activity sheet 1: This sheet gives experience of adding and subtracting 9, 10 or 11, using strategies you have covered during the whole-class starting point.

Activity sheet 2: This sheet is a generic sheet. Fill it in as in Chapter 3 Activity sheet 2, but this time with +9, +10, +11, –9, –10 and –11. The children throw two dice and use the numbers to make a starting 2-digit number (or you could write the numbers and use the sheet with a range of ability groups). They work out the effect of adding or subtracting 9, 10 or 11 to a number.

Activity sheet 3: This sheet extends the children's understanding of adding or subtracting multiples of 10 and 2-digit numbers ending in 9 or 1.

◆ Plenary session

◆ Reinforce the strategy for adding and subtracting numbers ending with 0, 1 or 9 to any other number. Ask some children from each group to explain their method of working mentally.

◆ *"Remember when you are using subtraction you are finding the difference between the two numbers."*

◆ Further activities

◆ Give the children a 1–100 number line (metre rule) and two different coloured dice. One dice is thrown to get a start number and the second to get the difference number. The start number is written down and a sequence of numbers with a difference of the second number is generated, for example:

    6   11   16   21   26   31

What do they notice about the number differences?

◆ Extension

◆ Use a pack of playing cards (without the picture cards) placed face down on the table.

Each of two players turns over three cards and arranges them to make a 3-digit number. They find the difference between the two numbers.

◆ Support

◆ Two players take turns to throw a dice or use a blank dice with suitable numbers written on the faces. Each player makes a 'train' from cubes to match the number thrown. The player with the larger number must tell their partner what the difference is between the two 'trains'. If the answer is correct the difference can be broken off and kept. The winner is the person who has the longest train after they have had six turns.

38
©Hopscotch Educational Publishing

developing
Numeracy
Skills

Numeracy
Year 3/P4

◆ **Making patterns** ◆

Use a 100 square or number line to work these out.

Start number		+ 10	+ 9	+11
1.	6	16	15	17
2.	4			
3.	7			
4.		18	17	19

Try some taking away.

Start number		– 10	– 9	–11
5.	20	10	11	9
6.	15			
7.	18			
8.		9	10	8

Can you see a pattern?

◆ The pattern I can see is _____

_____

Use your 0–9 number cards to make some larger numbers.

Start number	– 10	– 9	–11
3 7	27		

✦ **Making patterns** ✦

✦ You need a set of 0–9 cards. Shuffle them and turn them over facedown on the table. Turn over the top two and use the numbers to make a 2-digit number.

✦ Put the number into each machine in turn and write the new number. Do lots more. What do you notice?

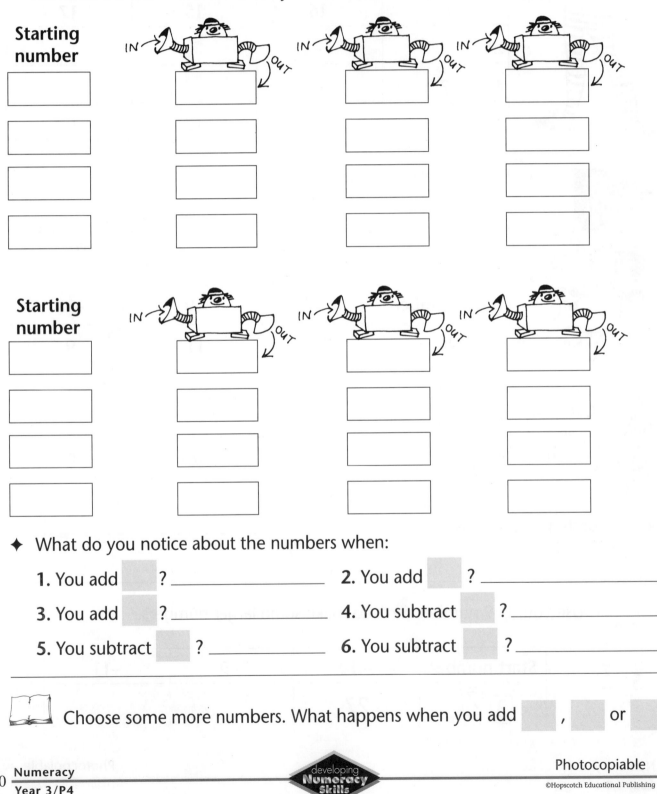

Starting number

✦ What do you notice about the numbers when:

1. You add ☐ ? _____ **2.** You add ☐ ? _____

3. You add ☐ ? _____ **4.** You subtract ☐ ? _____

5. You subtract ☐ ? _____ **6.** You subtract ☐ ? _____

Choose some more numbers. What happens when you add ☐ , ☐ or ☐ ?

developing **Numeracy Skills**

✦ **Making patterns** ✦

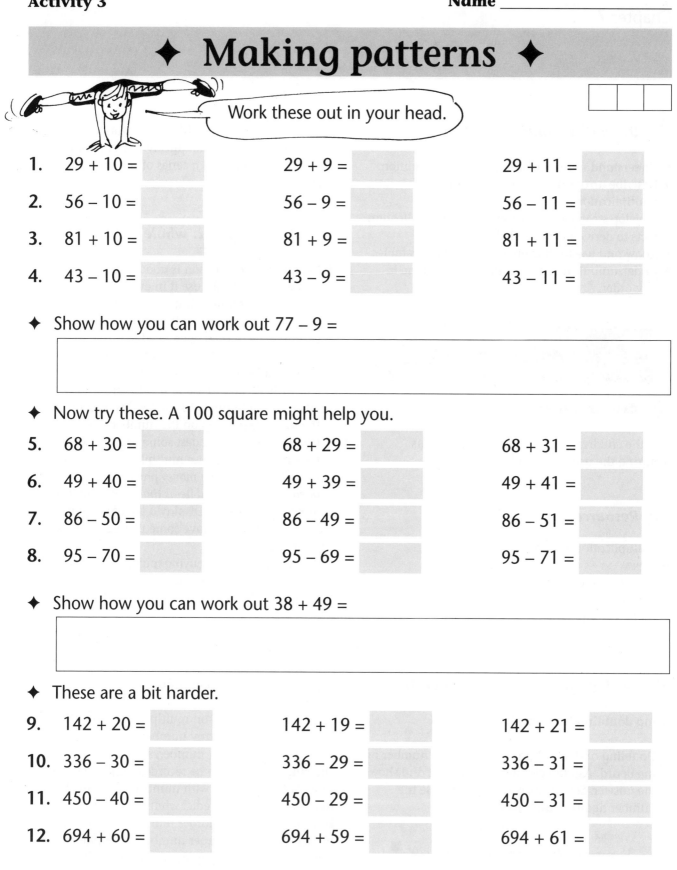

Work these out in your head.

1.	29 + 10 =	29 + 9 =	29 + 11 =
2.	56 – 10 =	56 – 9 =	56 – 11 =
3.	81 + 10 =	81 + 9 =	81 + 11 =
4.	43 – 10 =	43 – 9 =	43 – 11 =

✦ Show how you can work out 77 – 9 =

✦ Now try these. A 100 square might help you.

5.	68 + 30 =	68 + 29 =	68 + 31 =
6.	49 + 40 =	49 + 39 =	49 + 41 =
7.	86 – 50 =	86 – 49 =	86 – 51 =
8.	95 – 70 =	95 – 69 =	95 – 71 =

✦ Show how you can work out 38 + 49 =

✦ These are a bit harder.

9.	142 + 20 =	142 + 19 =	142 + 21 =
10.	336 – 30 =	336 – 29 =	336 – 31 =
11.	450 – 40 =	450 – 29 =	450 – 31 =
12.	694 + 60 =	694 + 59 =	694 + 61 =

Make up some 3-digit numbers. Add and subtract 100, 99 and 101.

Numeracy
Year 3/P4

developing
Numeracy
Skills

Photocopiable
©Hopscotch Educational Publishing

41

Multiplication

◆ Overall learning objectives

◆ Understand multiplication as repeated addition.
◆ Describe arrays using vocabulary of multiplication.
◆ Develop strategies for using known multiplication facts to derive new knowledge.
◆ Know and use facts from 2, 5 and 10 times tables.
◆ Understand that multiplication can be done in any order.

LESSON ONE
HOW MANY?

◆ Assessment focus

Can the children interpret real-life situations requiring the use of multiplication?

◆ Resources

◆ multiplication squares
◆ cubes
◆ squared paper
◆ 1–6 and 0–5 dice
◆ Diene's equipment
◆ money

◆ Oral work and mental calculation

Using doubling to multiply

◆ Doubling and doubling again. Write a number on the board. Ask the children to double it and show the answer. Say they are going to double the number again ... and again.

$$15 \xrightarrow{\text{x2}} 30 \xrightarrow{\text{x2}} 60 \xrightarrow{\text{x2}} 120$$

◆ Repeat this with other numbers and ask what is happening when numbers are doubled and doubled again. Help them to make the connection between doubling and multiplication. Give a mixture of numbers to double twice and

multiply by 4 for the children to work out mentally and respond quickly. Include some opportunities to add a series of the same number, such as 4 + 4 + 4 + 4...

◆ Starting point: whole class

◆ Explain that this lesson is about multiplication and when we might use it in everyday life. Remind the children that we use multiplication when equal numbers of things are needed. For example, 6 children each need to bring 10 coloured pencils to school and that this is the same as 10 + 10 + 10 + 10 + 10 + 10 and that we can write this as 10 x 6 or 6 x 10 and we say '6 lots of 10' or '6 times 10'. Show this as counting the same size of step on the number line.

◆ Can the children suggest some other times when they might need to use multiplication? *"Most of you will be working on money problems because we often buy several small items that are the same, such as packets of crisps."* Display a list of small items they might buy or have some pictures with prices under them.

◆ Ask questions about buying multiples of different items for the children to solve mentally. Remind them that doubling is the same as multiplying by 2.

◆ Group activities

          Focus group

Work with this group on multiples of 10 and the effect of multiplying any number by 10. Initially work with 10 sets of a number, such as 10 sets of 2, showing how this can be recorded on place value mats or boards. Start with numbers less than 10 but ask the children to predict what the answers might be if they multiplied larger numbers by 10. Can they model some of the larger numbers on a place value mat using Diene's equipment or cubes? This is a good time to use a calculator so that they can see the pattern of multiplying larger numbers by 10. Write some everyday problems together involving multiplication by 10, such as 10 toffee apples and 10 packets of crisps.

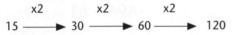

Multiplication

 Teacher-independent groups

Activity sheet 1: Tell these children that they might find it helpful to use money or coins, but to think how they might use doubling to help work out the prices for multiples of 'circus snacks'.

Activity sheet 2: This sheet also has some multiplication story problems but involving larger numbers. Again encourage the children to work mentally by using such strategies as doubling. Discuss strategies for using doubling to multiply by 4 to share at the plenary session.

LESSON TWO FINDING PRODUCTS

✦ Assessment focus

Can the children understand and use a variety of mathematical language for multiplication, for example describe equal 'sets of...' or 'lots of... '?

✦ Resources

✦ arrow cards
✦ cubes
✦ dice
✦ blank 100 square

✦ Oral work and mental calculation

Mixed calculations with place value

✦ The children will need sets of arrow cards and to work in pairs. Give addition and subtraction calculations using a variety of mathematical vocabulary. Write the numbers up if necessary. Tell them they need to make the answers with their cards and show you on the count of three.
"What is 20 more than 36?"
"What is 231 subtract 100?"
"What is the difference between 28 and 10?"
"How many more is 25 than 15?"

Activity sheet 3: Most of these story problems can be worked out using doubling and doubling again, or multiplying by 10. Encourage the children to use these strategies to find the answers mentally.

✦ Plenary session

✦ Invite children who did Activity sheet 2 to share some of their strategies for multiplying by 4. Children in the focus group can demonstrate what they have been learning about multiplication by 10.

✦ Starting point: whole class

✦ Draw an array on the board and ask the children to work in pairs and write some statements describing it. Write the statements on the board, adding any they might have missed out. Use the vocabulary of 'sets of ...' and 'lots of ...' as well as $3 + 3 + 3 + 3 = 12$, $4 + 4 + 4 = 12$, $3 (4) = 12$ and $4 (3) = 12$ and so on.

✦ Remind the class that this is called multiplication and write the symbol. Show how the array can be described using the x symbol, demonstrating that it can be written as 3 x 4 and 4 x 3. Say that in their work they will be using cubes to make rectangles like the one you have drawn and that you want them to use the multiplication symbol to write about the rectangles.

✦ Ask one of the children to come to the board, throw a large dice and make a 'stick' that length from cubes, for example 5 cubes long if 5 was thrown. Ask a second child to throw the dice and make that many 'sticks' the same length as the 5, for example 2 'sticks' of 5 if 2 is thrown. Draw the array and write the number statements using multiplication. On a large blank 100 square show how this array could be drawn and coloured. Repeat the dice throws and use a different colour to show these new numbers as an array on the 100 square. Tell group 2 that this will be their activity during the lesson.

©Hopscotch Educational Publishing

Multiplication

✦ Group activities

Focus group

Prepare some multiplication squares large enough for the children, working in pairs, to work out the answers and write them in the squares. Then ask them to model the answers using centicubes:

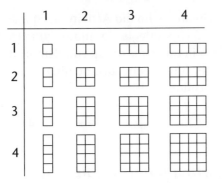

As they are working discuss the shapes the children are making. Why do they think all the models make rectangles and squares? Ask them to take a handful of cubes and try to make them into a square or rectangle, then draw the shape and write about it using words and numbers.

Teacher-independent groups

Group 1: Starting with a handful of interlocking cubes they will try to make a rectangle, so that if they pick up 15 cubes these can be made into a 5 x 3 rectangle or turned so that it becomes a 3 x 5 rectangle. Ask them to draw and record what they do in number sentences.

Group 2: Give each pair of children a 1–6 and a 0–5 dice. They should work in pairs on the activity from the starter, using a 100 square each. The aim is to be the first pair to colour the whole square and then write the products on each arrangement.

Group 3: This group works with the numbers 1–12 and, using each number in turn, makes as many rectangles for it as possible. Remind them that 2 x 1 can also be written as 1 x 2. Say that some numbers might make a lot more rectangles than others, such as 12. If time, extend the investigation up to 20.

✦ Plenary session

✦ Invite group 3 to share some of the things they discovered. In particular, which of the numbers between 1 and 12 had the most rectangle arrays. *"Could you predict which would be the next number to make a lot of different arrays?"*

✦ The focus group can show the chart they have made and explain how this can be used to find two facts from a pair of numbers. Explain how this links with division. If they know 3 x 4 and 4 x 3 equal 12, then 12 ÷ 3 = 4 and 12 ÷ 4 = 3.

✦ Further activities

✦ In pairs, the children could play the 'Dice multiplication game' (generic sheet 5, page 94). You need to put one number on each hat to go with the dice you use, so for 0–5 you need 0, 1, 2, 3, 4, 5, 6, then 8, 9, 10, 12 and so on. Vary the game with different dice and therefore different hat numbers.

✦ Make up games to practise multiplication facts on generic sheet 6 (page 95). Choose a table and write the multiples on the hexagons.

✦ Extension

✦ Can the children explain what is happening to the patterns on a calculator if they press 2 x = = =? How does this compare with pressing 2 + = = = ? (This might not work on all calculators.)

✦ Support

✦ Give the children some dot-to-dot pictures where multiples are joined instead of consecutive numbers, such as join 2, 4, 6, 8 and so on, or 5, 10, 15, 20 and so on.

✦ Circus puzzles ✦

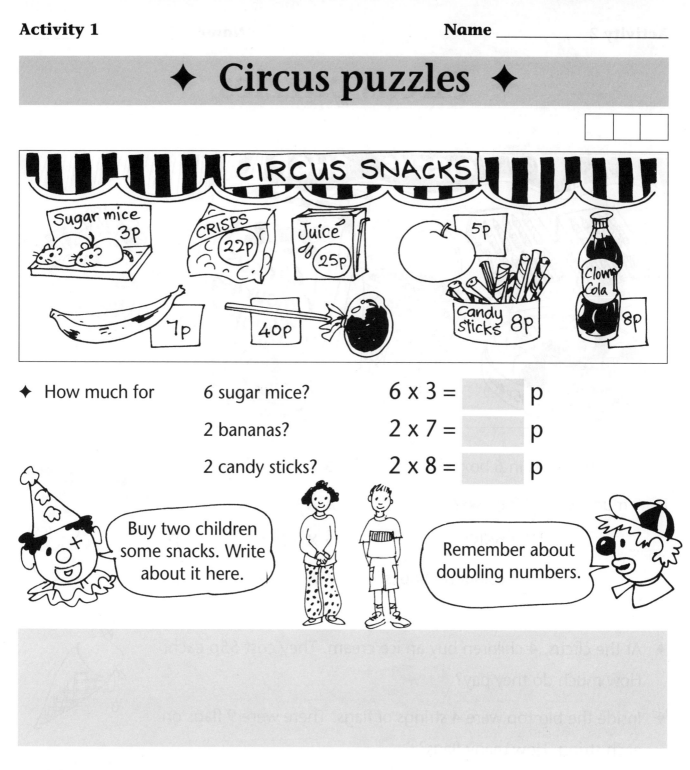

✦ How much for
    6 sugar mice? $6 \times 3 =$ ☐ p

    2 bananas? $2 \times 7 =$ ☐ p

    2 candy sticks? $2 \times 8 =$ ☐ p

Buy two children some snacks. Write about it here.

Remember about doubling numbers.

✦ If there are 10 children sitting in 3 rows at the circus, how many children are there? ☐

✦ Outside the big top were 4 baskets of flowers. There were 6 flowers in each basket. How many flowers were there? ☐

Write a multiplication story of your own.

©Hopscotch Educational Publishing

✦ Circus puzzles ✦

How many pencils in 6 boxes? $6 \times 10 =$ ☐

How much for   2 masks? $2 \times 45 =$ ☐ p

3 balls? $3 \times 15 =$ ☐ p

2 colouring books? $2 \times 50 =$ ☐ p

✦ At the circus, 4 children buy an ice cream. They cost 55p each. How much do they pay? ☐

✦ Inside the big top were 4 strings of flags. There were 9 flags on each string. How many flags? ☐

✦ Programmes for the circus cost 15p. How much will 5 programmes cost? ☐

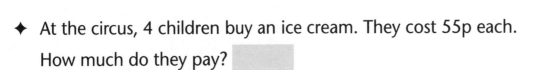

Write a story of your own like these.

developing
**Numeracy
Skills**

Activity 3

✦ Circus puzzles ✦

1. There were 10 children on the bus to the circus. The fares cost 50p each. How much did the tickets cost altogether?

2. On the bus, 2 people were sitting on every row of seats. If 19 of the rows were filled, how many people were on the bus?

3. At the fair, 4 children paid 75p to go on the big wheel. How much did they pay altogether?

4. The circus shop sold 5 clown cards in a pack. 7 children bought a pack each. How many cards did they buy?

5. Inside the big top were 8 strings of flags. There were 10 flags on every string. How many flags were there?

6. Programmes for the circus cost 35p. Mary bought 4 programmes. What did she pay for them?

7. At the end of the circus performance, the clowns came into the ring in 3 rows with 4 clowns in each row. How many clowns were there?

 Write some stories of your own like these.

Division reverses

♦ Overall learning objectives

♦ Develop an understanding of the relationship between multiplication and division.
♦ Multiply and divide by 1 and 10.
♦ Check calculations using inverse operations.
♦ Use multiplication strategies to solve division problems.
♦ Develop the vocabulary of division.

♦ LESSON ONE
BACK TO THE START

♦ Assessment focus

Can the children understand that division is the inverse of multiplication?

♦ Resources

♦ number lines
♦ large and small completed multiplication squares
♦ interlocking cubes
♦ dice
♦ number cards

♦ Oral work and mental calculation

Multiplying and dividing by 10

♦ Ask the children to think of the number 1 and then to multiply it by 10. What is the answer? Show how the numbers are written, emphasising that the numbers move one place to the left. Can they give the answer to 10 x 10? Show how the numbers move another place to the left and zero is used as a place holder in the units column. Can they work out mentally the answer to 2 x 10 and 20 x 10? Give them some more.
♦ Give some 2-digit numbers to be multiplied by 10 mentally. Turn the questions around so that you give, for example, 10 x 23 and so on. Can the children say how to divide multiples of 10 by 10? Ask for explanations of methods.

♦ Starting point: whole class

♦ Ask the children to make a 3 x 4 rectangle array of cubes and give them two or three minutes to talk with a partner about the number or word sentences they could write. Invite some children to write a number sentence on the board. Some of the things they might come up with are:

3 + 3 + 3 + 3 = 12	4 + 4 + 4 = 12
3 x 4 = 12	4 x 3 = 12
3 sets of 4 makes 12	4 sets of 3 makes 12
3 (4) = 12	4 (3) = 12

♦ Talk about the rows and columns in their 3 x 4 rectangle and ask them to divide it into 3 rows of 4. Show how this can be written as 12 ÷ 3. Remind them there are 12 cubes altogether and these can also be put into 4 rows of 3. Show how this arrangement is written as division. Invite a child to show this as hops forward in 3s along the number line and another to show it as hops of 3 going back. *"Which number did they start and finish on each time?"*
♦ *"Now let's reverse it and hop forward and back in 4s."* Write 12 ÷ 4. *"Now let's choose 2 more numbers and write 4 number sentences."* Show it as equal jumps on the number line. Leave this on display to help the independent groups later. Show the group 2 children how they can use a dice to find the numbers for their rows and columns.

♦ Group activities

Focus group

Use either large interlocking cubes or centicubes depending on the ability of the group. Ask the children to take a handful each and make them into a rectangle. Talk about the numbers in each row and column, then how this could be recorded as multiplication. Tell them to split the number into rows to write a division fact and into columns for another. Show how in multiplication either number can come first but not in division. They can cut the same size array from paper and use for a class display with the number facts written on it.

Division reverses

Teacher-independent groups

Group 1: Give these children some number cards that will make a rectangle array, for example:

Say that you want them to take a number card and to make a rectangle using that many cubes and to draw this in their books. Under the picture they write as many multiplication and division facts as they can about the arrays, breaking them down into equal sets if necessary.

Group 2: These children throw a dice to get the number of squares in a row and again for the number of rows. They draw the array and write the four multiplication and division facts under it.

LESSON TWO
NUMBER LINES AND SQUARES

◆ Assessment focus

Can the children use a wide range of vocabulary for division?

◆ Resources

- ✦ picture cards and number cards
- ✦ cubes
- ✦ 10–100 number line and a 100 square
- ✦ see-through containers

◆ Oral work and mental calculation

Linking doubling to multiplying by x2, x4, x8

✦ Write some 2-digit numbers on the board. Remind the children about doubling and halving numbers and give them some examples to calculate quickly. Can they make the link with multiplying and

Group 3: These children use their number cards face down on the table. They turn over two cards, use them to make a 2-digit number and multiply it by 10. They write the calculations in their books, together with the related multiplication and division facts, such as 37 x 10 = 370, so 10 x 37 = 370, 370 ÷ 10 = 37 and 370 ÷ 37 = 10. Ask them if they can multiply by 10 and then by 10 again. Can they show the new number facts?

◆ Plenary session

✦ Ask the children to explain the links between multiplication and division. Remind them that if they find one multiplication or division fact they should easily find three related facts. Ask for some quick mental responses to questions like, *"I know that 6 x 5 is 30, so what else do I know?"*

dividing by 2? Point to one of the numbers on the board and ask them to show you its double. Can they show you the answer if it is doubled again? Write the number with the two doubles on the board. Can children suggest another way of doing this? What if the number is halved and halved again? What is happening how?

✦ Challenge them to decide how to find the answer to 21 x 8 by using doubling. Ask them to work this out in pairs and then share their method with the class. Did anyone else do it the same way? Set some similar problems. Easier challenges can be given to those children who might need them.

◆ Starting point: whole class

✦ Display a large 0–100 number line and 100 square. Record some hops forward as '2 + 2 + 2 + 2 + 2 + 2 = 12', '6 lots of 2 steps makes 12'. Then show them how division 'undoes' that. Record '12 – 2 – 2 – 2 – 2 – 2 – 2 = 0' and write it on the board as '12 ÷ 2 = 6', or 'Start at 12, take hops of 2, you take 6 hops.' Do enough examples to get the group work going.

Numeracy

Year 3/P4

developing
Numeracy
Skills

49

©Hopscotch Educational Publishing

Division reverses

◆ Group activities

Focus group

Ask the children to use multiplication squares to show the answer to 5 x 4. After trying several examples, ask if they think the square can be used for division by starting with the answer to a multiplication problem. Try some examples. Give them some multiplication square problems and discuss how they might find the missing numbers.

x	5	8
		24
	35	

The numbers can be changed depending on the ability of the group. Encourage discussion between them as they find the solutions. What operation did they use to solve this problem? Ask them to write all the multiplication and division facts they can about the square they used. Can they set some similar problems for each other?

Teacher-independent groups

Activity sheet 1: These children use the number line on their sheet to draw equal jumps and record the number of jumps. They jump back using the same size jump and record this as multiplication and division facts. They continue with other equal-sized jumps forward and back, writing the number sentences each time.

Activity sheet 2: These children use a 0–30 number line for equal sized jumps forward and back. Ask for comments about the difference between jumping in 4s to 24 and back, then in 6s to 24 and back.

Activity sheet 3: This group uses a 1–100 number line or a 100 square to count on and back in equal groups.

◆ Plenary session

◆ *"What link there is between the four operations?"* *"You remember how subtraction can 'undo' addition. So what happens between multiplication and division?"*

◆ Ask group 1 to explain what they did using a number line to reverse multiplication. Group 3 can share how making equal jumps either forward or back between numbers on a 100 square does the same thing.

◆ *"What did you find easy today?"*

◆ *"Have you learned something new today?"*

◆ Further activities

◆ Use the blank function machines on page 40 (Chapter 6). The children input a number, double it and then halve it. Ask for comments.

◆ Play 'Clap the multiple'. If possible, have the children sitting in a circle. Decide who will start counting and the direction the counting will go. Tell them that instead of saying the number that is a multiple of 5, everybody must clap and the person will continue with the counting. Try having different starting places around the circle, going in different directions and using different multiples.

◆ Extension

◆ Again use the blank function machine on page 40 (Chapter 6). Numbers are doubled twice and then they have to find the number to divide by to get back to the original number, for example 3 x 2 → 6 x 2 → 12 ÷ ? → 3.

◆ Support

◆ Do some practical sharing activities in the classroom, for example *"I have 6 pieces of paper. How many pieces can 3 children have?"*

◆ Equal jumps ◆

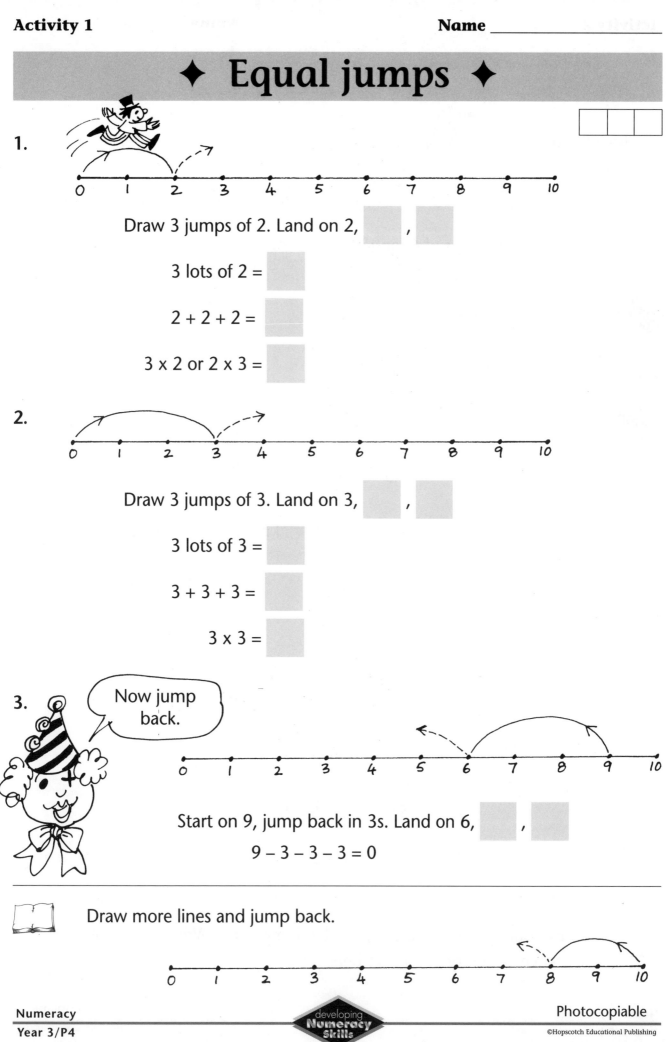

1.

Draw 3 jumps of 2. Land on 2, [ ] , [ ]

3 lots of 2 = [ ]

2 + 2 + 2 = [ ]

3 x 2 or 2 x 3 = [ ]

2.

Draw 3 jumps of 3. Land on 3, [ ] , [ ]

3 lots of 3 = [ ]

3 + 3 + 3 = [ ]

3 x 3 = [ ]

3.

Now jump back.

Start on 9, jump back in 3s. Land on 6, [ ] , [ ]

9 − 3 − 3 − 3 = 0

Draw more lines and jump back.

◆ Equal jumps ◆

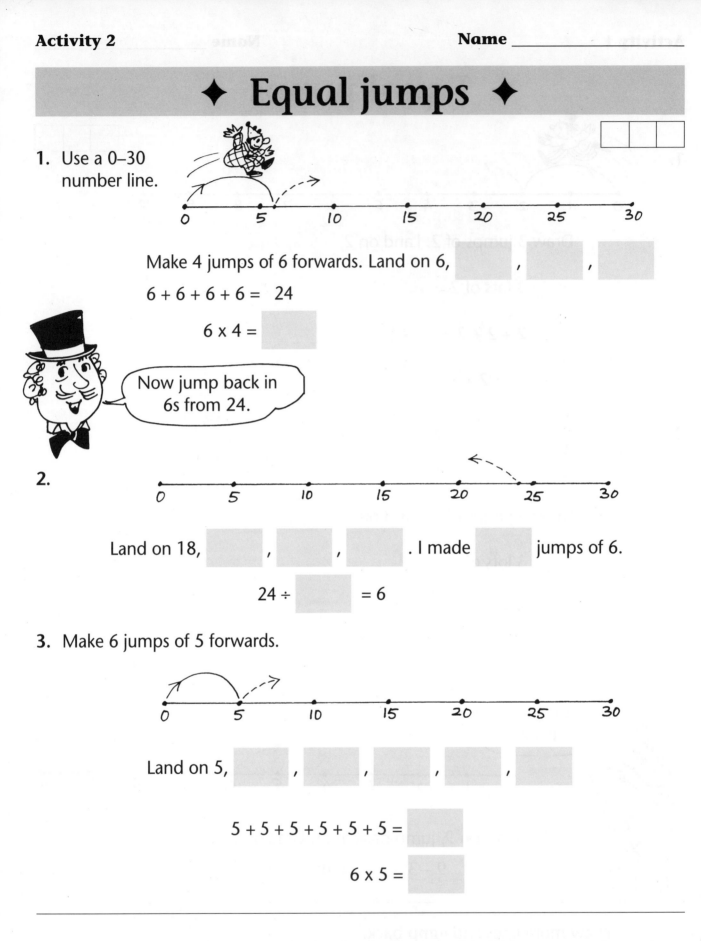

1. Use a 0–30 number line.

Make 4 jumps of 6 forwards. Land on 6, ▢ , ▢ , ▢

$6 + 6 + 6 + 6 =$ 24

$6 \times 4 =$ ▢

Now jump back in 6s from 24.

2.

Land on 18, ▢ , ▢ , ▢ . I made ▢ jumps of 6.

$24 \div$ ▢ $= 6$

3. Make 6 jumps of 5 forwards.

Land on 5, ▢ , ▢ , ▢ , ▢

$5 + 5 + 5 + 5 + 5 + 5 =$ ▢

$6 \times 5 =$ ▢

Draw your own line and jump back 6 jumps of 5. Write a ÷ number sentence. Then try other numbers.

developing
Numeracy
Skills

✦ Equal jumps ✦

✦ Use a 1–100 number line or a 100 square.

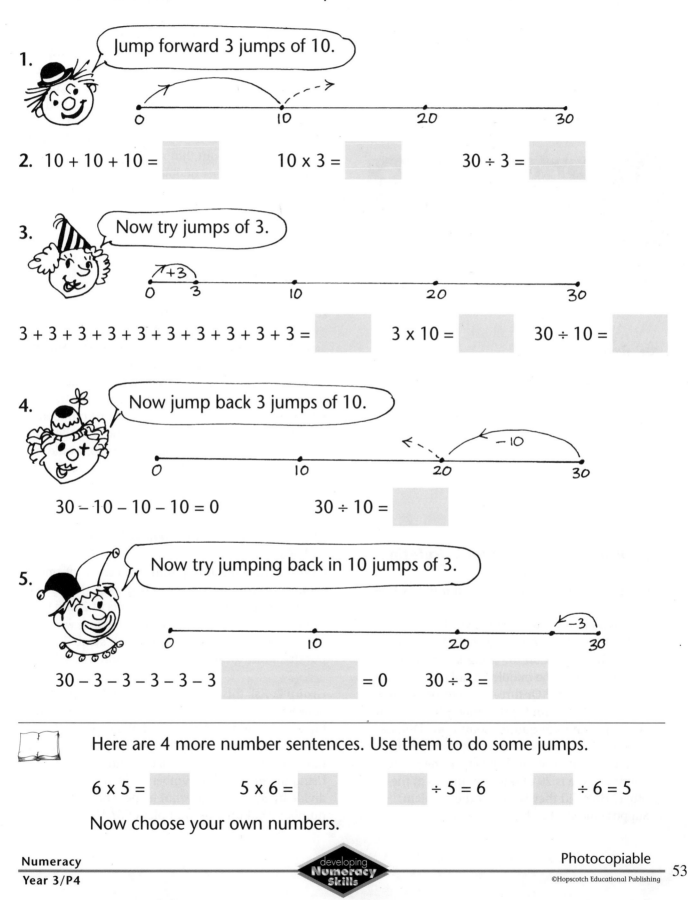

1. Jump forward 3 jumps of 10.

2. 10 + 10 + 10 = ☐   10 x 3 = ☐   30 ÷ 3 = ☐

3. Now try jumps of 3.

3 + 3 + 3 + 3 + 3 + 3 + 3 + 3 + 3 + 3 = ☐   3 x 10 = ☐   30 ÷ 10 = ☐

4. Now jump back 3 jumps of 10.

30 − 10 − 10 − 10 = 0   30 ÷ 10 = ☐

5. Now try jumping back in 10 jumps of 3.

30 − 3 − 3 − 3 − 3 − 3 ☐ = 0   30 ÷ 3 = ☐

Here are 4 more number sentences. Use them to do some jumps.

6 x 5 = ☐   5 x 6 = ☐   ☐ ÷ 5 = 6   ☐ ÷ 6 = 5

Now choose your own numbers.

Division and remainders

✦ Overall learning objectives

✦ Develop an understanding of division as both repeated subtraction and sharing.

✦ Solve 'real life' problems using division.

✦ Use whole number remainders in division.

✦ Make decisions about rounding answers up or down.

✦ LESSON ONE ✦ LEFTOVERS

✦ Assessment focus

Can the children understand whole number remainders?

✦ Resources

✦ interlocking cubes

✦ small 'counting' items

✦ long rod (approx 1m) marked with quarter points

✦ Oral work and mental calculation

Approximating and ordering on a number line

✦ Attach a piece of paper with 0 written on it to one end of the rod and a piece with 100 written on it to the other end. Can the children say which number goes in the middle? What about quarter of the way along? Or three quarters of the way? Change the start and end numbers to 0 and 1000. What goes at each quarter point now? Discuss how this is the same or different from the first problem. What are the numbers at the quarter points if there is 20 at one end and 40 at the other? How did they work out the problem? Suppose the start is 2 and the end is 4?

✦ Starting point: whole class

✦ You will need a large area to introduce this lesson. Ask the children to divide into pairs with any left over coming to stand by you. Discuss the number of groups of 2 that can be made with everyone in the class and how many left. Get the children to regroup in 3s and again see if any are left. Continue with an increasing number of children to a group. Explain that sometimes when they are dividing a number of objects into equal sets there might be some left over and that these are called the remainder. Show them how this is written as a number sentence.

✦ Group activities

 Focus group

Tell the group that they will work in pairs. Using one hand they will each take some cubes. If the cubes can be grouped in 2s with none left over, they can score 2. If the cubes can be grouped in 3s with none left over, they can score 3. If they can be grouped in 4s... and so on. Do this up to 9s. What number of cubes, including, but not bigger than 20, would they most like to take? Help the children to record some of their findings.

Teacher-independent groups

Group 1: Give this group some collections of small numbers of counting items in bags. Ask them to find out if these can be put into equal sets of 2 and to draw pictures of what they have done and write number sentences, using the division symbol. Then put them into groups of 3 to draw and write.

Group 2: Ask this group to find out which numbers between 1 and 20 will divide exactly by 2 and which have a remainder. They should discuss what the remainder is likely to be. Suggest they use cubes to make arrays showing the factors and remainders. Using the same set of numbers, which of them divide by 3, and again what is the remainder for the numbers that are not multiples of 3? They continue

Division and remainders

by finding the numbers that divide by 4, then 5 and so on. Can they show what they have done using division number sentences?

Group 3: Tell this group to imagine they have 24 biscuits and you want them to find out how these could be shared equally between different numbers of children. Encourage them to record what they have found out as drawings and as division sentences. Help them to understand that by working out one fact, such as 24 makes 6 groups of 4 (24 ÷ 6 = 4), they can find that 24 also makes 4 groups of 6, (24 ÷ 4 = 6). Which numbers between 1 and 24 divide exactly and which leave a remainder?

 *Plenary session*

✦ *"Who can tell us which operation you have been using today?"*
✦ *"Yasmeen, tell us something about remainders."*
✦ *"Some numbers are 'good' numbers for dividing. 24 is a 'good' number. Who can tell us another one?"* (12 divides in many ways.)
✦ Discuss whether or not there are any links between the work done by the groups. Finish by posing some simple mental division problems, both with and without remainders.
✦ *"What did you enjoy in maths today?"*

LESSON TWO
THE LEFTOVER BIT

 **Assessment focus**

Can the children make sensible decisions about rounding up or down?

"Start on 0 and make 4 hops of 3, hold up the number you land on."
"Start on 21 and go back two hops of 10. What number are you on?"
"Start on 5. How many hops of 5 will you need to reach 20?"
"Start on 9 and make 2 hops of 10. What number did you land on?"

✦ Resources

✦ number lines
✦ money
✦ egg boxes, muffin tins, cake boxes and so on.

✦ Starting point: whole class

✦ Explain that when doing division we sometimes have to decide whether to round up or to round down. Use the tables in the classroom as an example. These often seat either 6 or 4 depending on their shape. Relate the activity to your own class. *"There are 28 children in the class and they can sit 6 to a table. How many tables will be needed?"* Explain that the number of tables has to be rounded up so that everyone has a place.
✦ Give an example of rounding down. *"A child has 55p to spend on stickers. How many packs costing 10p each could be bought?"* Explain why the remainder is rounded down in this instance.
✦ Give more examples of each situation, asking the children to explain whether the answer has to be rounded up or down and why this is the case.

✦ Oral work and mental calculation

Multiplication and addition on the number line

✦ Ask the children to picture a 0–30 number line in their heads, although less able children can be given a number line to work with. Ask them to imagine that their finger is on the 0 and they are going to make hops of 2 until they reach 10. They should hold up a card to show how many hops of 2 they made.

Division and remainders

◆ Group activities

Focus group

Use the collection of containers such as different-sized egg boxes. Tell the children that they have, for example, 20 eggs that need to be packed in boxes of six and you want them to find out how many boxes will be needed for that many eggs. How might they record what they have done both in pictures and in numbers? What if the same number of eggs are to be packed with 12 in a box? Continue by working with different numbers and size of grouping. Explain that for most of this work they are rounding the numbers up because all the eggs or cakes need to be put into containers. Give them an instance of where rounding down is more appropriate, for example *"I have 50p, so how many sweets costing 15p can I buy?"*

Teacher-independent groups

Activity sheet 1: This worksheet requires the children to make decisions about rounding numbers up or down depending on the situation. For some of the questions it might help if the children use money or practical equipment to help them make decisions about the remainders.

Activity sheet 2: This requires the children to make the same type of decision as those in group 1.

Activity sheet 3: This has similar problems of rounding up and down but uses larger numbers.

◆ Plenary session

◆ *"George, did you round up or down for that problem? Why?"*
◆ *"Nicky, tell us your chocolate egg story."*
◆ Can any of the children think of times when they use division in their everyday lives?
◆ *"What did you find hard today? Do you understand it now, or should we do more problems tomorrow?"*

◆ Further activities

◆ Read *When the Doorbell Rang* by Pat Hutchins. This is about two children who are going to share 12 biscuits, when the doorbell rings and a friend arrives so, then they have to share between three children and it continues with more friends arriving. Ask the children to illustrate the sharing aspect of the story and write the number sentences to match the pictures.
◆ Find out some of the times they use division at home, for example sharing out the cutlery to lay the table or dividing a packet of biscuits between members of the family.
◆ Explore division with remainders on a calculator. For example, enter the number 48 and subtract 5. How many times can 5 be subtracted? What number is left in the calculator?

◆ Extension

◆ Ask the children to explore the factors of other multiples of 12 and to make some general observations about the results.

◆ Support

◆ Use generic sheet 6 (page 95) with numbers 2, 4, 6, 8, 10, 12, 9, 15, 18, 20 and 24, and a coin with a sticker saying '3 groups' on one side and '2 groups' on the other side. Toss the coin in turns to find out how many groups to divide into, then choose a number on the hexagon to divide so that there is no remainder. *"So if you toss '3 groups' you might choose hexagon 15. Cover 15 with your colour counter."*

✦ How many? ✦

1. 17 balloons. How many children

   can have 3 balloons? ▢ children.

   Draw them.

2. 13 buns. How many children

   can have 3 buns? ▢ children.

   Draw them.

3. Toby has 30p.

   The helter-skelter costs 12p.
   How many rides can he have?

   ▢ rides.

4. In the picnic area 6 people can sit at a table.
   How many tables for 13 people?

   ▢ tables.

Make up a story about chocolate eggs packed
in boxes of 6.

Chocolate Eggs

developing
Numeracy
Skills

Activity 2 **Name** ______________

✦ How many? ✦

1.

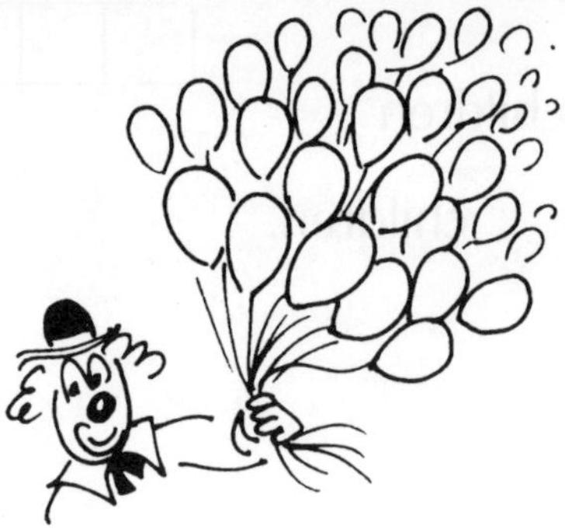

The clown has 37 balloons.
How many children can have 5 balloons?

☐ children.

2. 17 buns. How many children can have 3 buns?

☐ children.

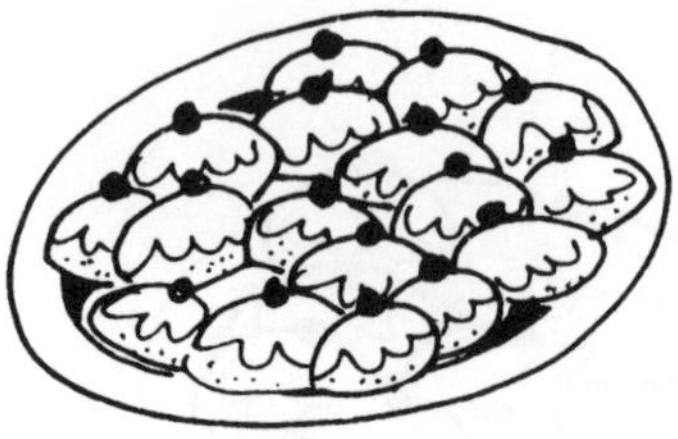

3. Sheena has 85p.

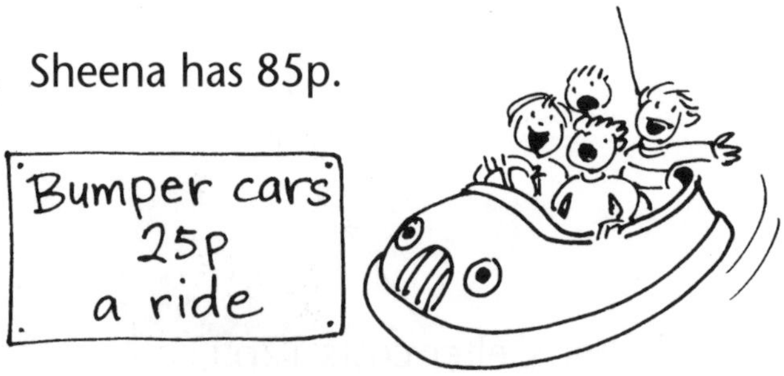

Bumper cars
25p
a ride

How many rides can she have?

☐ rides.

4. 31 children are going to the circus. 3 children can sit in a row. How many rows are needed?

☐ rows.

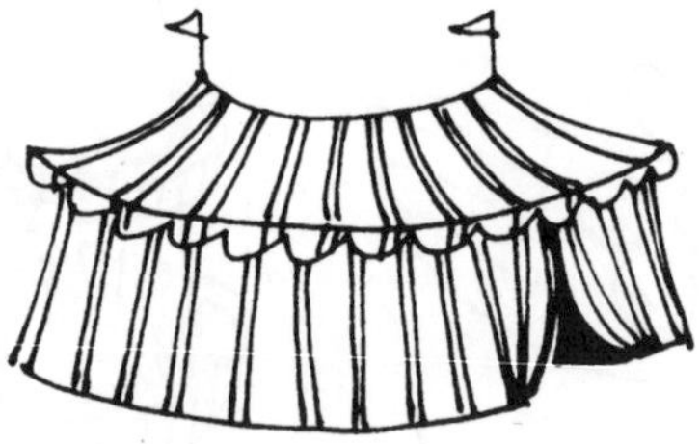

5.

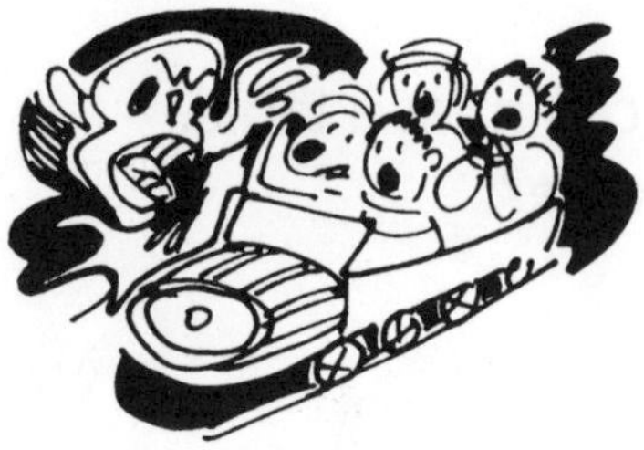

29 people are in the queue.
4 people to a carriage.
How many carriages are needed?

☐ carriages.

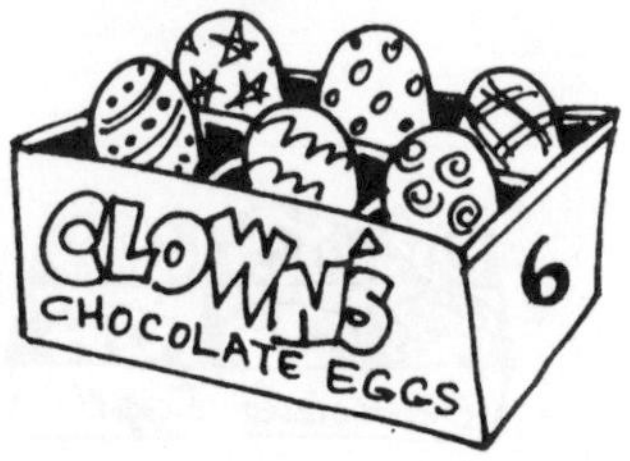

CLOWN'S
CHOCOLATE EGGS
6

Clown's chocolate eggs are packed 6 in a box. How many boxes are needed for 31 children to have an egg each?

Make up another chocolate egg story.

✦ How many? ✦

1. 31 children are going to the circus. If a minibus takes 16 children, how many minibuses will they use?

   [ ]　minibuses.

2. The clown has 56 balloons. He makes them into bunches of 10. How many full bunches will he make?

   [ ]　bunches.

3. Lubna has £3. She wants to ride on the Big Wheel. It costs 45p for a ride. How many rides can she have?

   [ ]　rides.

4. There are 80 scoops of ice cream in a tub. If 3 scoops are put into every cone, how many cones can be made?

   [ ]　cones.

5. The clown wants to make some stilts. He has 63m of wood and each pair is made from 4m of wood. How many pairs of stilts can he make?

   [ ]　pairs of stilts.

Clown's chocolate eggs are packed 6 to a box. Choose a number over 100 and tell a story of how to pack those eggs.

developing Numeracy Skills

Fractions

✦ Overall learning objectives

✦ Recognise that a fraction is an equal part of a whole shape or a number.

✦ Recognise and name common fractions, such as $\frac{1}{2}$, $\frac{1}{4}$, $\frac{1}{8}$ and $\frac{1}{10}$.

✦ Recognise simple equivalent fractions, such as $\frac{1}{2} = \frac{2}{4} = \frac{4}{8}$.

✦ Compare and order fractions.

✦ Develop the language of fractions.

✦ LESSON ONE
WHO HAS MOST?

✦ Assessment focus

Can the children identify and name common fractions?

✦ Resources

✦ paper squares, rectangles and circles

✦ Oral work and mental calculation

Linking multiplication and division

✦ Write up this equation: ☐ x 2 = ☐. There is an infinite number of possible answers! Ask the children for some answers and then ask them to say how they worked them out. Then write up another one: ☐ x ☐ = 50 (or another number); again ask for suggestions. When they have made some suggestions, again ask them how they did the calculation. Focus with them on how division is needed to solve these equations.

✦ Starting point: whole class

✦ Each child needs a paper rectangle. Ask them to fold the rectangle into half making another rectangle. Discuss how they know what is half and remind them that both halves need to be the

same. Ask them to fold the shape again and open it out. How many pieces are there now? Are they all the same size? Show them how to write a quarter and ask them to write this on each piece.

✦ Fold the paper back into quarters and fold again. Again, count the pieces and ask what these might be called and how an eighth might be written. Ask them to write an eighth on the back of each fraction of the paper.

✦ Play 'Show me the fraction'. *"Show me half. Fold the paper so you can see that fraction."* Continue with other fractions. *"Show me two-eighths."* Ask for the equivalent in quarters and how many eighths are left. *"Show me two quarters. How many halves is that? How many eighths is that?"*

✦ *"Fold a square in half. Does everyone have the same shape? How many ways can the square be folded in half?"* (A rectangle and a triangle.) Continue by folding in quarters and eighths. With folding squares some children may end up with just rectangles and others with triangles, so share the different shapes. Finish with folding a circle into eighths. *"Which of the fractions is largest and which smallest?"* Then look at the fraction notation. *"Why it is that the one with the largest denominator (the number at the bottom) is the smallest fraction?"*

✦ Group activities

Focus group

Continue with folding paper to help the children identify equivalent fractions using halves, quarters and eighths, then to record either with gummed paper shapes or by drawing. This will help them to show practically that $\frac{2}{4}$ is the same as $\frac{1}{2}$ and so on.

Teacher-independent groups

Activity sheet 1: Following on from the introduction this group should colour quarters and halves of shapes on their sheet.

Activity sheet 2: This is the same as Activity sheet 1 except that $\frac{3}{4}$ is used and the children will need to think about different ways of colouring $\frac{1}{2}$.

60
©Hopscotch Educational Publishing

developing
Numeracy
Skills

Numeracy
Year 3/P4

Fractions

Activity sheet 3: This group will work with equivalent fractions and some comparisons of fractions. They should identify fractions of a shape that are coloured and those that are not coloured to develop an understanding of complementary fractions, for example $\frac{3}{8}$ and $\frac{5}{8}$ together make a whole.

✦ LESSON TWO
NUMBER LINE FRACTIONS

✦ Assessment focus

Can the children use a number line for fractions?

✦ Resources

✦ fraction number lines
✦ washing line, large 0–10 cards, blank cards and large felt-tipped pen
✦ number lines

✦ Oral work and mental calculation

Mixed mental calculations

✦ Write the numbers 3, 5 and 9 on the board and tell the children they will have only three minutes to try and make as many numbers as possible between 1 and 10. They can use addition and subtraction or multiplication and division but no other numbers. The numbers can be used more than once and in any order. Start by showing ways of making 1 (such as $9 - 5 - 3 = 1$). Set the timer and after three minutes ask them to count how many answers they found. Write a selection of the calculations on a large sheet of paper and ask them to add more later.

✦ Plenary session

✦ Ask some of the children what they have learned about fractions and whether it is possible to have such a thing as a bigger half of something. Stress that each fraction of a whole is the same size and write the equivalent fractions on the board. For example, 1 is the same as $\frac{2}{2}$, $\frac{4}{4}$ and $\frac{8}{8}$.
✦ Finish the lesson by returning to the folded rectangles from the introduction. Ask questions about complementary fractions. *"If I can see one quarter, how much can't I see?"*

✦ Starting point: whole class

✦ Prepare a long 'washing line'. Ask some children to put cards numbered 1–10 on it in the correct place, with wide spaces between. Ask the class questions involving fractions *"What comes halfway between 2 and 3?"* and *"Write the number halfway between $10\frac{1}{2}$ and 11"*. They can write the answers on blank cards and hang them in place on the line. Continue until all the halves and quarters between 0 and 10 have been written. Practise counting along the number line using the whole numbers and the halves. Can the children continue counting beyond the numbers on the line? Now count along the number line using all the fractions. What comes next on the number line?
✦ Explain that they will be making their own number lines during the lesson and tell them how long the lines will be and the fractions to mark. Show group 1 on the board how to start their line and tell them what their activity will be. Tell the other two groups what they have to do.
✦ Show the children how they can record the halfway numbers on a blank number line.

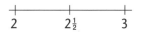

Fractions

◆ Group activities

Focus group

The children need to start by making a fraction number line to 10 that includes the halves and quarters. Ask them to find half of some of the numbers, such as half of 8 and then ask how they would find quarter of a number. Explain that finding a half of a half is the same as finding a quarter. Ask if they can find a quarter of all the numbers up to 10. Encourage them to work systematically, starting with 1. Once those are found they can continue by finding three-quarters of all the numbers.

Teacher-independent groups

Group 1: Give each child a long strip of paper. Ask them to draw a long line, mark where 0 comes and then write all the numbers up to 5 equally spaced out. Next they write in all the halves. Using only their 0–5 cards they turn over two cards and find the number that comes halfway between them.

$3\frac{1}{2}$ is halfway between 2 and 5.

Group 2: This group should use a number line from 0–10 and mark the halves, using the fraction number line to help if necessary. Using a set of 0–10 cards, two cards are turned over and they find the halfway point between them on their number line.

Group 3: This group needs to make a 0–10 number line marked with quarters as well as halves. They will also need to make a set of cards of all the halves between 0 and 10 to go with their 0–10 cards. As with the other groups they turn over two cards and find the halfway point between them. The answers will involve quarters as well as halves.

◆ Plenary session

◆ Ask group 3 to share with the other children what they had to do. Use the 'washing line' to demonstrate how they found some of the halfway points, especially ones like halfway between $6\frac{1}{2}$ and 10.

◆ *"Let's count in halves from zero to 10: 0, $\frac{1}{2}$, 1, $1\frac{1}{2}$, 2 and so on."*

◆ *"What did you do today that you found easy?"*

◆ *"What was difficult? Why do you think people found that dificult?"*

◆ Further activities

◆ Do more paper folding to demonstrate equivalent fractions.

1 whole							
$\frac{1}{2}$				half			
$\frac{1}{4}$		$\frac{1}{4}$		$\frac{1}{4}$		$\frac{1}{4}$	
$\frac{1}{8}$	$\frac{1}{8}$	$\frac{1}{8}$	$\frac{1}{8}$	$\frac{1}{8}$	$\frac{1}{8}$	$\frac{1}{8}$	$\frac{1}{8}$

"I can see that $\frac{2}{8}$ is the same size as $\frac{1}{4}$."

◆ Extension

◆ Extend the Lesson Two, group 3 activity to using a 0–20 number line and cards 0–20, including halves.

◆ Support

◆ Give the children activities that involve working with halves and quarters. Fraction dominoes or snap games will help them recognise some equivalents and to match pictures of fractions with their notation.

✦ Colour the fractions ✦

1. Colour $\frac{1}{2}$.

2. Colour $\frac{1}{4}$.

3. Colour $\frac{1}{2}$.

4. What fraction is shaded?

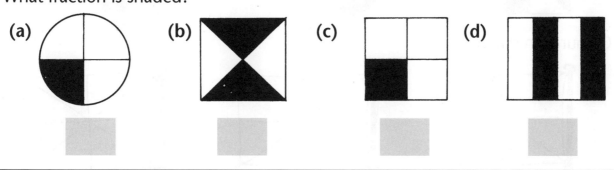

(a)   (b)   (c)   (d)

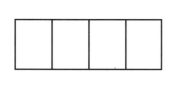  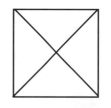 Use 2 red and 2 blue cubes. Make different $\frac{1}{2}$ red and $\frac{1}{2}$ blue shapes. Draw and colour the shapes.

◆ Colour the fractions ◆

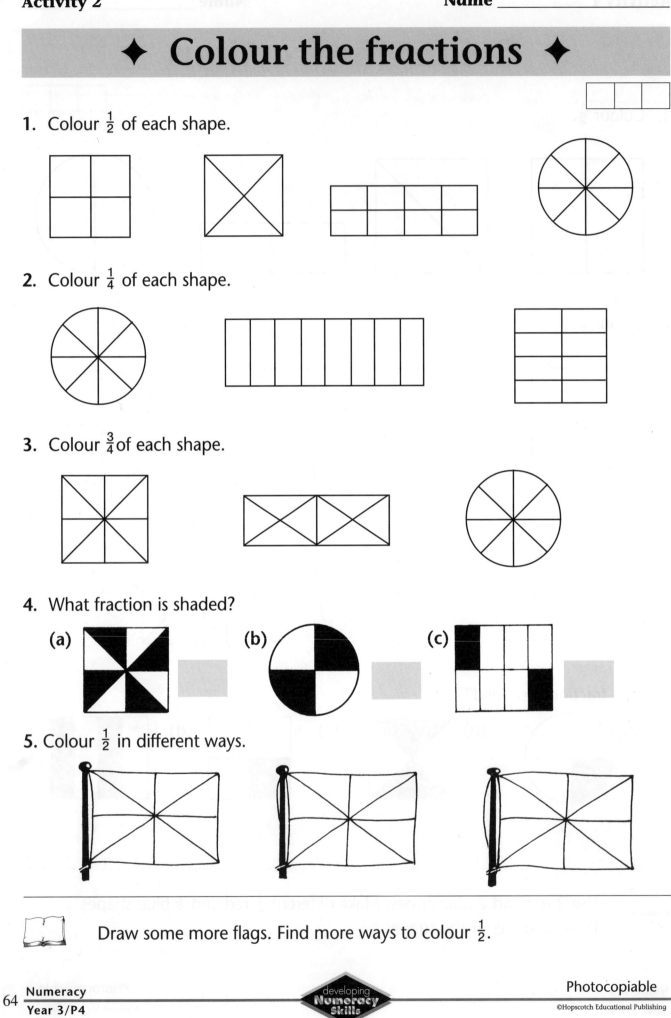

1. Colour $\frac{1}{2}$ of each shape.

2. Colour $\frac{1}{4}$ of each shape.

3. Colour $\frac{3}{4}$ of each shape.

4. What fraction is shaded?

   (a)　　　　　　　(b)　　　　　　　(c)

5. Colour $\frac{1}{2}$ in different ways.

Draw some more flags. Find more ways to colour $\frac{1}{2}$.

Photocopiable
©Hopscotch Educational Publishing

✦ Colour the fractions ✦

1. Colour $\frac{1}{2}$ in different ways.

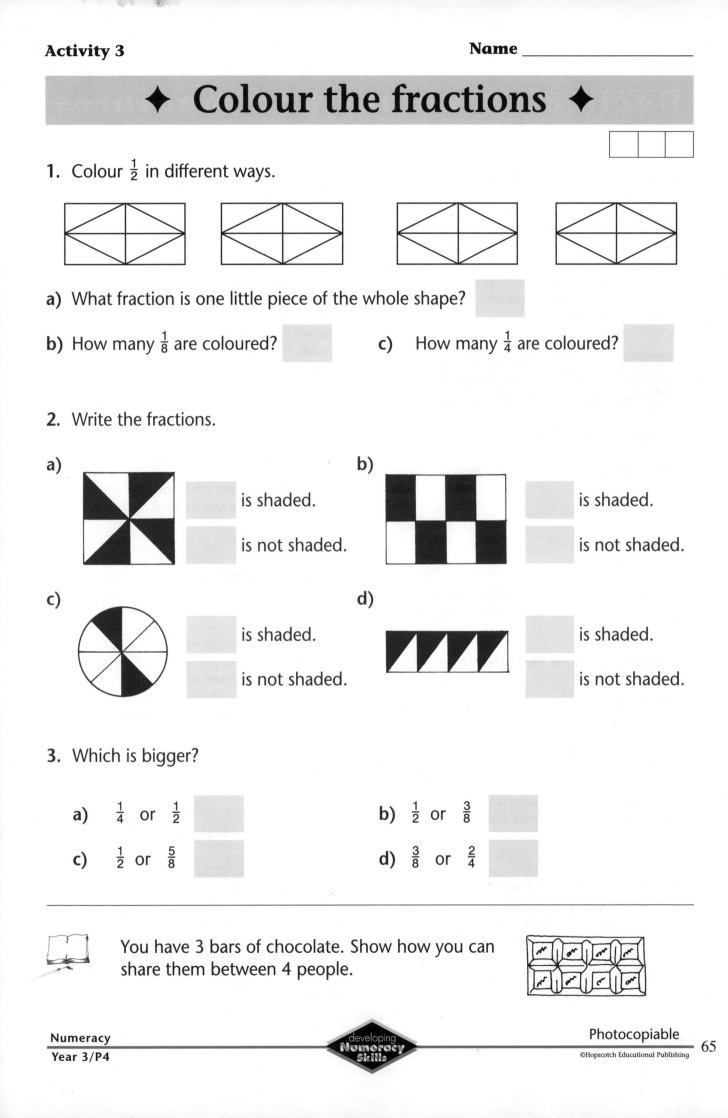

a) What fraction is one little piece of the whole shape?

b) How many $\frac{1}{8}$ are coloured?   **c)** How many $\frac{1}{4}$ are coloured?

2. Write the fractions.

a)   is shaded.

                             is not shaded.

b)   is shaded.

                             is not shaded.

c)   is shaded.

                             is not shaded.

d)   is shaded.

                             is not shaded.

3. Which is bigger?

a) $\frac{1}{4}$ or $\frac{1}{2}$ **b)** $\frac{1}{2}$ or $\frac{3}{8}$

c) $\frac{1}{2}$ or $\frac{5}{8}$ **d)** $\frac{3}{8}$ or $\frac{2}{4}$

You have 3 bars of chocolate. Show how you can share them between 4 people.

developing Numeracy Skills

Decimals – money and measures

✦ Overall learning objectives

✦ Develop an understanding of decimal notation in money and linear measurement.
✦ Use an increasing range of vocabulary to explain word problems and their solutions.
✦ Recognise the value of both coins and notes.
✦ Work with metres and centimetres and know the relationship between them.

✦ LESSON ONE POUNDS AND PENCE

✦ Assessment focus

Can the children recognise and use decimal notation in money?

✦ Resources

✦ money (real coins if possible)
✦ a collection of small toys and other items such as rubbers and pencils displaying their real prices

✦ Oral work and mental calculation

Equal grouping

✦ Choose a number, such as 24 or 48 or 100, and ask the children to suggest ways to split the number up into equal groups, for example 24 splits into 6 equal groups of 4. Repeat this several times over a few weeks using different numbers, showing how multiplication and division are linked.

✦ Starting point: whole class

✦ Begin the session by discussing why it is important to be able to work with money. Ask the children how prices are written in shops. Can they say what is the significance of each digit in the price?

✦ Write some prices on the board both as pence only and as a decimal with the £ symbol. Invite the children to explain the difference. Reinforce the fact that the first number to the right of the decimal point represents the 10 pences and the next one shows the pennies. Ask some children to write the other representation of the price under the ones you have written and to say the two ways of writing them. *"Today we will be doing work that will need you to think about both ways of writing the cost of things."*

✦ Prepare a money place value board for group 1 to use with number cards.

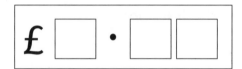

Explain that all their prices are below £1, so they will always have a zero in the £ column, for example £0.35.

✦ Group activities

    Focus group

Give these children a collection of small toys/items marked with their real prices (depending on the group's ability). Ask them to work out how much change they would get from a given amount if each item was bought on its own. Can they say the answers using decimals and as pence? *"Show me the coins you could use to pay each time."* Continue by asking them to 'buy' more than one of each item or several different items and working out the cost.

    Teacher-independent groups

Activity sheet 1: This group would benefit from having real objects, with their prices, for them to handle and number cards to put on the money place value board so that they can all agree how to write a price. They will also need some money (preferably real) to help with calculations. The aim is to develop their understanding of decimal notation but they need the opportunity to work practically with money.

Decimals – money and measures

Activity sheet 2: This sheet contains some more expensive items. While it is important to encourage the children to work mentally, they might still need to be able to use money to solve problems, including pound coins. You might need to discuss with them the operation they would need to answer the questions about how much more change.

Activity sheet 3: The amounts of money in these questions are more demanding than for the other two groups. Encourage these children to work mentally or with paper and pencil jottings as much as possible. Discuss the methods they have used to share during the plenary session.

LESSON TWO
WHAT'S THE LENGTH?

◆ Assessment focus

Can the children solve problems with linear measures?

◆ Resources

◆ money (real coins if possible)
◆ a collection of toys and items such as rubbers, pens and pencils displaying their real prices
◆ rulers, metre sticks, tape measures, height measure

◆ Oral work and mental calculation

Calculating differences

◆ Give the children practice in finding small differences between numbers mentally, especially between 3-digit numbers. Ask them questions such as:
"How many more must be added to 246 to make 250?"
"What must be taken from 700 to make 695?"
"What is the difference between 359 and 365?"

◆ Plenary session

◆ Ask group 3 to share some of their informal methods for calculations with money. Stress again the importance of being able to work out money problems.
◆ Give some addition and subtraction problems for them to work out mentally, aiming specific questions at each group. Group 1 can be given problems involving change from £1 to help reinforce number bonds to 100, while the other groups can be asked to give change from larger amounts.
◆ *"Tell me something you enjoyed doing today."*

◆ Write the numbers on the board each time because it can be difficult to remember two large numbers. Encourage them to share their strategies for finding answers. Give some easier questions for those children who need them and some extra challenging ones for the more able.

◆ Starting point: whole class

◆ Start by reminding the children about the ways of writing money as either £ and pence or just pence and what the numbers represent depending on their position. Show a metre stick and the centimetre divisions along it. Explain that metres and centimetres can be recorded in a similar way to money, so that 2 metres and 30 centimetres can also be written as 2.30 metres. Write some measurements on the board using decimal notation and invite them to say how many metres and centimetres each one shows. Give some measurements the other way round and ask how these will be written as decimals. Include measurements of less than a metre, such as 29cm written as 0.29m.
◆ Tell them that they will be measuring lengths of different things and they will be using these measurements to work out problems. As an example, measure the width of a piece of paper and say, *"How could I find how wide 4 pieces of*

Decimals – money and measures

paper are without measuring them?" Let them explain their ideas and discuss which would be the best method. *"What about 10 pieces?"*

◆ Group activities

Focus group

Tell the children they are going to find out how much wood they need to make a pair of stilts so they are one metre taller. Discuss what stilts are like. *"How high up a person's body do they come?"* Help them to decide the rules for measuring one stilt and recording the outcome in metric units and decimals. Observe the children carefully and listen to the methods they use.

Teacher-independent groups

Group 1: Give this group some lengths of different-coloured ribbons slightly more than a metre in length. Ask them to measure the ribbons carefully and to write the lengths as m and cm. Can they find the combined length of two ribbons? Encourage them to work in pairs on part of the activity because they will probably need to use two metre sticks. Tell them to think about explaining their method of working ready to explain it in the plenary session.

Group 2: This group starts by measuring one table in the room and records in metres and centimetres, then decimals. Give them the problem of finding how far two of the tables would stretch if they were put in a line. What about all the tables in the room?

Group 3: Working in pairs, these children should measure their heights, recording them in metres and centimetres and as decimals. If you have a height measure in school, make that available. Ask them to work out how tall they would be if a circus clown worked some magic on them and they shrank to half their size. How long would their arms be if they shrank as well? Can they draw a picture of themselves with the new measurements shown, using both forms of recording?

◆ Plenary session

◆ Ask group 1 to explain their methods for finding the combined length of two pieces of ribbon. Write on the board the length of each piece of ribbon and the total as a decimal. Some children might have measured end to end; others might have a different method.

◆ Ask a pair from group 2 to share their methods for finding multiple lengths with the tables.

◆ *"Jubeen, work out half of 1m 20cms. Tell us how you did that."*

◆ Further activities

◆ If the children only have 2p and 5p coins in their money box, how can they make all the possible amounts of money between 1p and £1.00? Which amounts cannot be made?

◆ Ask them to collect some till receipts from home shopping trips. Look at how the prices are written and write them as pence.

◆ Extension

◆ Give the children some catalogues and say they have £20 to spend. Can they find different ways of buying a present for everyone in their family?

◆ Support

◆ Put some money on a large sheet of paper in the middle of the table. The children take turns to throw a dice and collect the number of pence shown and record the amount on a piece of paper. On the second turn they start to keep a running total. After six turns they say how much they each have and discuss who has the greatest amount. Can they exchange their 'winnings' for a smaller number of coins?

✦ The circus shop ✦

1. Write the prices in £ and p.

£ _____   £ _____

£ _____   £ _____

2. Write these answers in pence.

2 balloons cost _____ p.   2 candy sticks cost _____ p.

and   1 van and 1 balloon cost _____ p.

3. You have _____ .

How much change if you buy 1 _____ ? _____ p change.

Buy more things with £1 and write how much change.

✦ The circus shop ✦

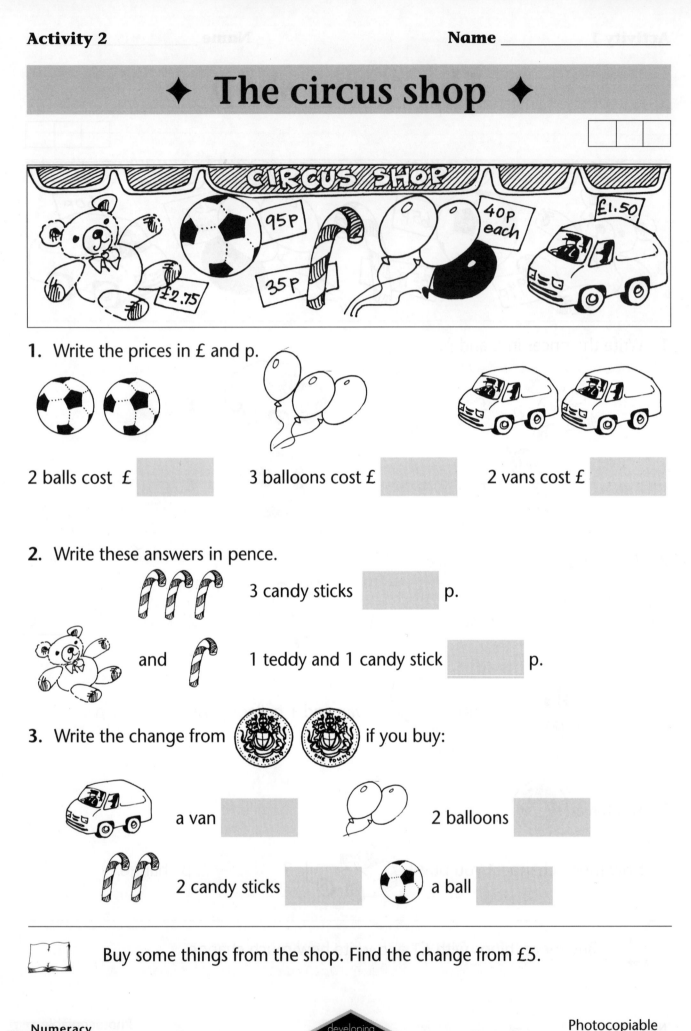

1. Write the prices in £ and p.

2 balls cost £ [   ]   3 balloons cost £ [   ]   2 vans cost £ [   ]

2. Write these answers in pence.

3 candy sticks [   ] p.

and   1 teddy and 1 candy stick [   ] p.

3. Write the change from [coins] if you buy:

a van [   ]   2 balloons [   ]

2 candy sticks [   ]   a ball [   ]

📖   Buy some things from the shop. Find the change from £5.

Photocopiable

©Hopscotch Educational Publishing

✦ The circus shop ✦

CIRCUS SHOP

95p

40p
each

£4.95

£2.75

35p

£1.50

1. Write your answers in £ and p.

4 balloons cost £ _____

a ball and a van cost £ _____

2 teddies cost £ _____

2. Write your answers in pence.

A ball costs _____ p more than a balloon.

A teddy costs _____ p more than a van.

A clown suit costs _____ p more than a teddy.

3. Write the change from £5 if you buy:

a clown suit _____   a balloon _____

a van _____   a teddy _____

4 balls _____   5 balloons _____

You have £10 to buy party presents for 4 friends. You need to
buy 4 of each present. How will you spend your money?

developing
Numeracy
Skills

Measures – 1

◆ Overall learning objectives

◆ Use, read and write a range of vocabulary of length and mass.
◆ Know and use the relationship between kilometres, metres and centimetres, kilograms and grams.
◆ Solve problems relating to measurement.
◆ Make reasonable estimates and check by measuring with increasing accuracy.
◆ Develop an understanding of the approximate nature of measurement.

◆ LESSON ONE — MEASURE IT

◆ Assessment focus

Can the children use equipment for linear measuring?

◆ Resources

◆ tape measures, rulers, metre sticks, decimetres (Diene's apparatus or 10 centicubes) and so on
◆ string

◆ Oral work and mental calculation

Number bonds of 100

◆ Practise adding pairs of numbers that total 100. Display a large 0–99 square for all the children to see. Point to a number on the square, such as 56, and ask the children to hold up the number that must be added to make 100. Show how they can use the 100 square to count down in 10s and then go right or left to adjust. Encourage them to work quickly as you point to other numbers on the square. Give easier examples if necessary, for example *"What goes with 11 to make 20?"*

◆ Starting point: whole class

◆ Explain that all the groups will be measuring length today and ask the children to suggest the units they might use for different activities, as this will help them to choose the measurements to work with. Write a table on the board showing the relationship between the units they could choose and ask what equipment they would need for each one.

1	centimetre
10	decimetre
100	metre
1000	kilometre

◆ Ask questions like, *"If I had to measure the windows for new curtains which units would I use?"*, *"What equipment would I need?"* and *"I want to go to London (or a place nearby) so how do I measure the distance?"* Show a small picture and say, *"I need a frame for this picture. What units will I use?"* Show the children how decimetres can be used for measuring in groups of 10cm.
◆ Explain to the groups that they will be finding different measurements of themselves. As group 1 will be comparing pictures of themselves, ask what they think they need to do. *"Where will you start to measure and where will you finish?"* If the children decide to use rulers, show how to use them correctly, starting at 0 and not at 1 or the extra bit at the end.

◆ Group activities

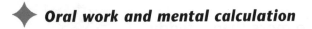

Focus group

These children will be finding how far they can jump with both feet together. Talk about the need for a common starting point. Let one child jump and discuss whether that is more or less than a metre. Show how they could measure the first part of their jump with a metre stick and estimate the number of centimetres beyond that they jumped, writing the full estimate on a large piece of paper. Once the jump is measured that can be recorded with the estimate. Compare the set of jumps and discuss whether the metre stick helped.

Measures – 1

Teacher-independent groups

Group 1: Each child has a piece of strong paper. They draw themselves as tall as possible and cut out the picture. They then measure the height of the picture. Exchange pictures with a partner. Is the measurement the same? Can they put all the pictures in order and make a display with them showing the measurements?

Group 2: These children work in pairs. They take turns to draw around a hand (with fingers closed) of the other person as carefully as possible. Each pair writes their estimate, on a large piece of paper, of how long they think a piece of string needs to be to go all round the pencil line. Tell them to write on the paper whose hand they think will need the longer piece of string and who will need the shorter. Still working in pairs, they measure all round the drawing with a length of string, cutting it when they have finished. The string is measured and compared with the estimate. Each pair can compare their hand perimeters and work out the difference between them. Extend the activity by asking the children to find out if their foot perimeter is longer or shorter than their hand.

Group 3: These children are to find out which of them has the longest full span measured from thumb tip to little finger tip. They work in groups of three to cut a length of string equal to the person's span to get a more accurate measurement. They should record and compare all their measurements in both metres and centimetres. Then they put the measurements in order. Can they each work out how many of their full spans equal the length of the classroom?

◆ Plenary session

◆ Ask the focus group to say whether they thought they got better at estimating part of their jumps that were a bit more than a metre. Why do they think that? *"Which units do you think are easiest to estimate in, metres or centimetres?"*

◆ Group 2 can share their work. *"Was it easy to measure round a person's hand? Where you surprised by the length of the perimeters?"*

◆ Remind the children how measurements can be recorded, for example 2m 24cm, 224cm or 2.24m. Write some examples on the board. Include 65cm = 0.65m. Give some measurements in centimetres and ask the children for the equivalent in metres, for example 269 cm = 2 m 69 cm.

LESSON TWO HOW HEAVY?

◆ Assessment focus

Can the children make reasonable estimates and check by measuring?

◆ Resources

◆ balances and weights
◆ collections of books and other items for weighing

◆ Oral work and mental calculation

Mixed mental calculation

◆ Use a set of 1–9 cards and invite four children to turn over one number each. Write the four numbers on the board. Working in groups of four the children should write as many calculations as possible using those numbers in one minute. Set the timer. Ask each group for a different calculation and write them on the board, until all their answers have been shared. How many did each group write? What else could be done? Repeat this with four different numbers.

Measures – 1

Starting point: whole class

✦ Put some 1kg, 100g, 50g, 10g and 1g weights on the tables for the children to handle. Can they suggest things that might be weighed using each of them? Remind them that 1000g is the same as 1kg. Demonstrate how to use a balance correctly, ensuring the two pans balance before starting to weigh. Give each table some pairs of scissors and ask them to estimate which of the weights it is nearest. *"Is it about the same as 100g?"* Let the children hold the scissors in one hand and the 100g in the other. Share the estimations and test with the balance. Ask how to find the difference between one of the estimates and the actual weight. Stress the importance of estimation and when we might need to use it.

✦ Tell the groups that they have different things to weigh during the lesson but before using the balances they must balance with their hands, then write their estimates on the worksheets. Say you want them to work out the differences between the estimation and the actual weight. Show how this could be done using the balances.

◆ Group activities

 Focus group

These children will be finding things that weigh 10g. They should start by collecting some small objects, such as centicubes, pencil sharpeners, rubbers and polystyrene packaging. (It is important to have something large but light.) Working in pairs, ask them to estimate how much/many of each thing

they think will balance a 10g weight. Talk about how they decided. Let them test their predictions and make a chart together of the cubes and so on that balanced 10g.

Teacher-independent groups

Activity sheet 1: Remind these children to balance with their hands and estimate first before using the balances. (They could do this simply by comparing one object with another.) If they draw their weights this will help you to check their addition.

Activity sheet 2: These do the same as group 1, but they estimate the weight in grams before they find the actual weight. They need five books weighing less than a kilogram and to number them 1–5.

Activity sheet 3: This group needs six books weighing about 1kg and to number them 1–6. They will need to write their estimates in grams and the actual weights in a table.

◆ Plenary session

✦ Ask the focus group to show their display of things that balance 10g. Why do children think that some of the items take up more space than others?
✦ *"How did you estimate the order?"*
✦ *"Did the size make a difference?"*
✦ *"Were light things easier to estimate than heavy things?"*
✦ End with some mental conversions from grams to kilograms and grams.

◆ Further activities

✦ How far can a ball be kicked/thrown or a paper aeroplane fly?

◆ Extension

✦ Estimate and measure how far people have to walk from their seat to the playground. How far do they walk if they have 3 play times?

◆ Support

✦ Give further practical experience with both estimation and balancing. You could make that part of your oral maths every day for a week.
✦ Give the children help with adding up the weights used for balancing.

Name _____

✦ How heavy? ✦

✦ Measure.

     book   **cube**   **shoe**   **housebrick**   **full pencil case**

1. Estimate and draw in order.

lightest   heaviest

2. Now weigh them. Draw and write down the weights you used.

3. Draw the order.

lightest   heaviest

Find 2 more things to weigh. Estimate first.

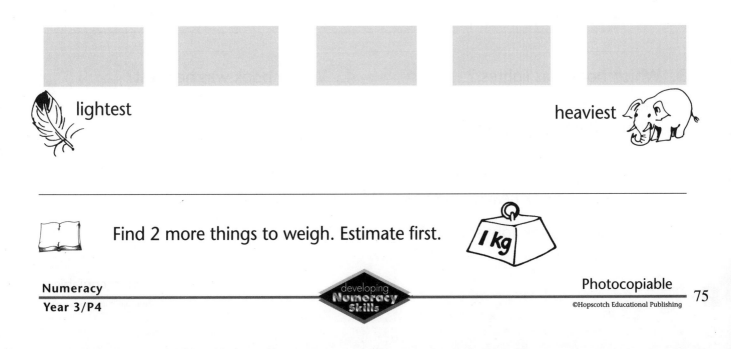

✦ How heavy? ✦

✦ You need:

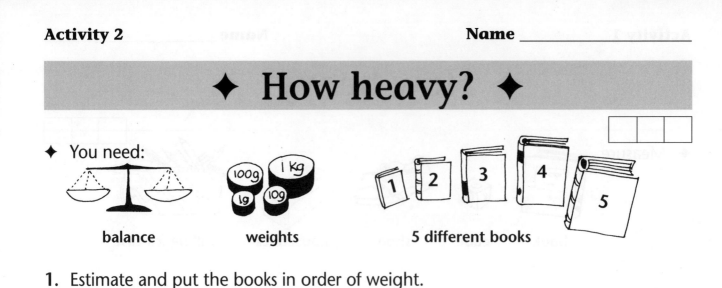

balance   weights   5 different books

1. Estimate and put the books in order of weight.

lightest   heaviest

2. Estimate and weigh the books. Find the difference between the estimate and the weight.

Estimate	Weight	Difference
1 g	g	g
2 g	g	g
3 g	g	g
4 g	g	g
5 g	g	g

3. Which book was lightest?   4. Which book was heaviest?

5. What is the difference in weight?

Find a book heavier than 1kg. What does it weigh?

Find a book lighter than 100g. What does it weigh?

Name _____

✦ How heavy? ✦

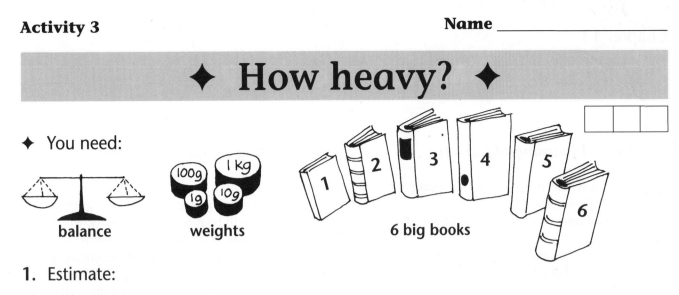

✦ You need:

balance   weights   6 big books

1. Estimate:

a) Which books weigh more than 1kg? _____

b) Which books weigh less than 1kg? _____

2. Estimate and weigh the books in grams. Complete the table.

	Estimate	**Weight**	**Difference**
Book 1			
Book 2			
Book 3			
Book 4			
Book 5			
Book 6			

3. Which book was heaviest?   **4.** Which book was lightest?

5. What is the difference in their weights? _____

6. Write the six weights in order.

    g   g   g   g   g   g

The heaviest letter you can send for 19p weighs   g.

How many pieces of paper is that with an envelope?

How can you find out?

Measures – 2

◆ Overall learning objectives

✦ Begin to make decisions about the appropriate units for measurement.
✦ Develop an understanding of the usefulness of estimation.
✦ Select and use suitable measuring equipment.
✦ Read scales, labelled and unlabelled, to the nearest division.
✦ Solve problems relating to measurement.

◆ LESSON ONE WHAT'S IN IT?

◆ Assessment focus

Can the children use suitable units for measuring capacity?

◆ Resources

✦ empty bottles in a variety of sizes and shapes (with labels removed)
✦ funnels, measuring jugs and cylinders
✦ containers, such as margarine tubs or plastic cups
✦ sand, centicubes, rice or lentils
✦ graduated cylinders
✦ plastic bottles and cups

◆ Oral work and mental calculation

Calculating measures mentally

✦ Do some mental calculations on measurement.
"I want some ribbons half a metre long. How many can I cut from 6 metres?"
"My recipe needs 250 grams of flour. I want to make double the recipe. How much flour?"
"Mum buys wallpaper 26 metres long. How many pieces 2 metres long can she cut?"
"A car is driven at 50 miles an hour. How far does it travel in half an hour? How far in 2 hours?"
✦ Each time ask children to explain the type of calculation they used.

◆ Starting point: whole class

✦ Remind the children about the units they have used for measuring length and mass. In this lesson they will be measuring capacity, which is measuring how much a container holds. They will be finding out about the capacity of different things. Write on the board '1000 millilitres = 1 litre' and discuss this. Let them handle measuring jugs and cylinders with different scales and say which would be best for measuring certain amounts. *"Which would be the best container to measure what this little bottle contains? Why?"*
✦ Tell them that they are to use different methods to find the capacity of different containers. Show them how to fill a container, pour the contents into a measure and read the amount. They are to write how many millilitres they use each time. Groups 2 and 3 will use small containers to calculate the capacity of larger ones. Stress the need to be as accurate as possible.

◆ Group activities

Focus group

Give the children a collection of bottles in assorted shapes and sizes. Tell them their task is to find out the capacity of each one but first they must decide which holds the least and which holds the most. Allow time for discussion as the containers are ordered, especially if there are some unusual shapes. Invite suggestions about the best way to test the capacity of each. You could make available only 100ml graduated jugs or cylinders, depending on the group's ability. After measuring the bottles ask if there are any surprises. Why did some bottles seem to hold more than others?

Teacher-independent groups

Group 1: Each pair of children will need a container (such as a margarine tub), materials to measure with and a graduated cylinder. Ask them to find the capacity of the container by filling it with, for instance, sand, then pouring the sand into the measuring cylinder and reading the scale.

Measures – 2

"Does the container have the same capacity even if it is filled with different things?"

Group 2: This group will need some large bottles with a strip of paper glued down the side, a funnel and a 100 ml measure. They work in pairs to write the scale up the side of the bottles graduated in 100ml. Ask them to find the total capacity of the bottles. They will share their methods in the plenary session.

Group 3: Using large bottles and plastic cups, ask this group to work in pairs to find out the number of plastic cups that can be filled from their one large bottle. By finding the capacity of the plastic cup can they calculate the capacity of the bottle? *"How many cups of juice could the circus cafe get from different sized containers, such as a 5 litre container?"*

◆ Plenary session

✦ Ask group 2 to show their bottles marked into 100 ml divisions. Ask the children to explain how they worked and answer questions such as *"How many millilitres are there in half your bottle?"* and *"How high up the bottle will 350ml come?"*

✦ Did group 1 find that the capacity of their container was the same even when filled with different things? Remind the children they have been measuring capacity, or what a container will hold, and they need to remember that the units they have used are litres and millilitres.

✦ Demonstrate how to write in ml and litres, for example 350ml and 0.35l.

LESSON TWO READING SCALES

◆ Assessment focus

Can the children read a variety of scales, labelled and unlabelled?

◆ Resources

✦ coins, preferably real
✦ letter scales, bathroom scales and cooking scales
✦ number lines showing different divisions
✦ spring balances
✦ tape measures, surveyor's tapes

◆ Oral work and mental calculation

Calculating money mentally

✦ Ask the children to imagine they have a pile of money in front of them and they are picking up certain coins to add. Can they imagine they have

picked up a 20p coin, then a 10p, a 20p and a 1p. How much money is that? Give the answer in pence; then in £. Ask a child to write the answer on the board. Continue with other combinations:
"Pick up £1, then another £1, then 50p. How much do you have?"
"Pick up 50p, another 50p, then 20p and 20p. How much have you?"
"You give three 20 pence pieces to the shopkeeper. You have a 5p change. How much did you spend?"

◆ Starting point: whole class

✦ Draw a selection of number lines on the board with different scales to represent ways of measuring length, mass and capacity. Also show some of the different measuring equipment they might find, and discuss how they are marked. Remind the children about the units they will be using for the three types of measurement.

✦ If they have not experienced the spring balance scales much before, ask where they might see dials like this. They might mention clocks, dials on cookers or in cars. Explain that dials are just like number lines except they go round.

Measures – 2

✦ Indicate different places on the scales for the children to read and give some measurements for them to mark, giving reasons for the decisions. Explain that they will be writing some more measurements like this during the lesson. Use the examples on the board to show them that they can write intermediate values on the scales if it helps.

◆ Group activities

Focus group

Use different types of spring balances with a variety of scales, together with a collection of things from the classroom for the children to weigh. It is not a good idea to weigh children as this might cause distress. Discuss which type is best for different purposes. Ask the children to use each balance to weigh something and draw the item on the scales, together with the reading. Underneath the picture they write the weight of the item. Help the children to read the scales accurately.

Teacher-independent groups

Activity sheet 1: This activity sheet follows from the starter activity. It entails the children reading measurements using different scales to represent

length, capacity and mass. They might be helped by having some examples of different ways of numbering scales available to them.

Activity sheet 2: This is a similar sheet to Activity sheet 1 except that they have to read the scales to the nearest division, rather than the whole numbers. Question 3b requires grams written as 0.35kg.

Activity sheet 3: This has higher numbers and the scales are more complex.

◆ Plenary session

✦ Return to the scales used for the introduction. Invite the children to compare those scales with the ones on their worksheets. Which ones were the hardest to do and for what reason? Were there some easy ones? Did some of the children find writing more numbers helpful? Finish the session by using a string number line with numbers representing a scale pegged to it. Indicate points along the line and ask, *"Where do you think 120 should go?"* or *"What number would come halfway between 50 and 100?"*

"What comes here?"

◆ Further activities

✦ Use surveyor's tapes to measure long distances, such as the size of the netball court or the football pitch.
✦ Use spring balances for weighing collections. *"Find the heaviest potato in this bag."*

◆ Extension

✦ Find the mass, length or capacity of a single item. For example, use a spring balance to find the mass of a tennis ball and calculate the mass of ten balls and check with the balance.

◆ Support

✦ Give practical experience of reading scales, for example in cooking, and reading temperatures on a thermometer.
✦ Use washing lines to represent dials and scales using varied numbers, as on the activity sheets, and target specific children in oral maths time.

◆ Measure it ◆

1. How long is the rope?

a)

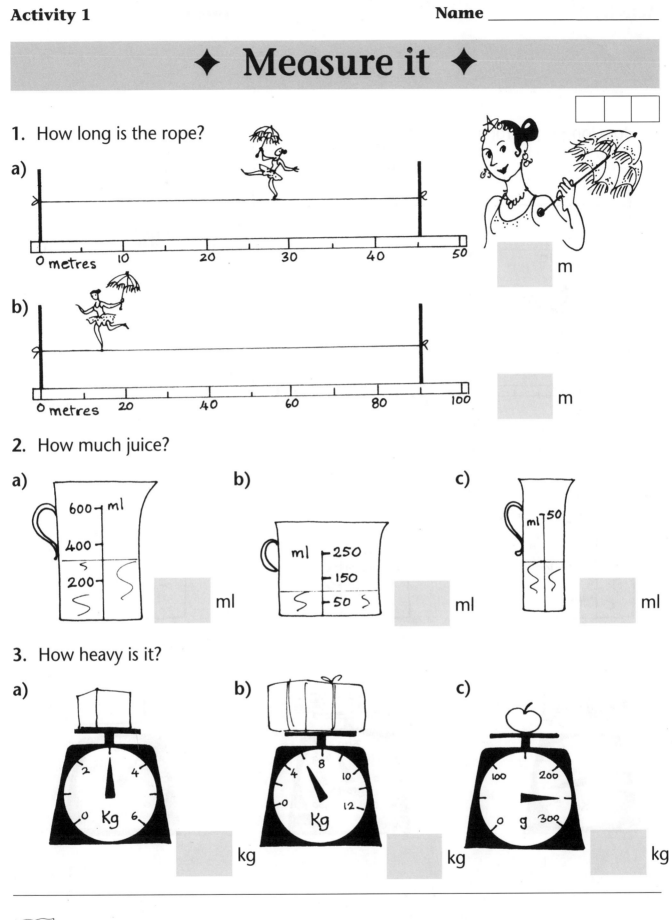

0 metres   10   20   30   40   50

[ ] m

b)

0 metres   20   40   60   80   100

[ ] m

2. How much juice?

a)   600 ml 400 200   [ ] ml

b)   ml   250 150 50   [ ] ml

c)   ml 50   [ ] ml

3. How heavy is it?

a)   2   4   0 Kg 6   [ ] kg

b)   8   4   10   0   12   Kg   [ ] kg

c)   100   200   0 g 300   [ ] kg

Put 200ml of water in a 1 litre measure. Draw the jug and show the water level.

◆ Measure it ◆

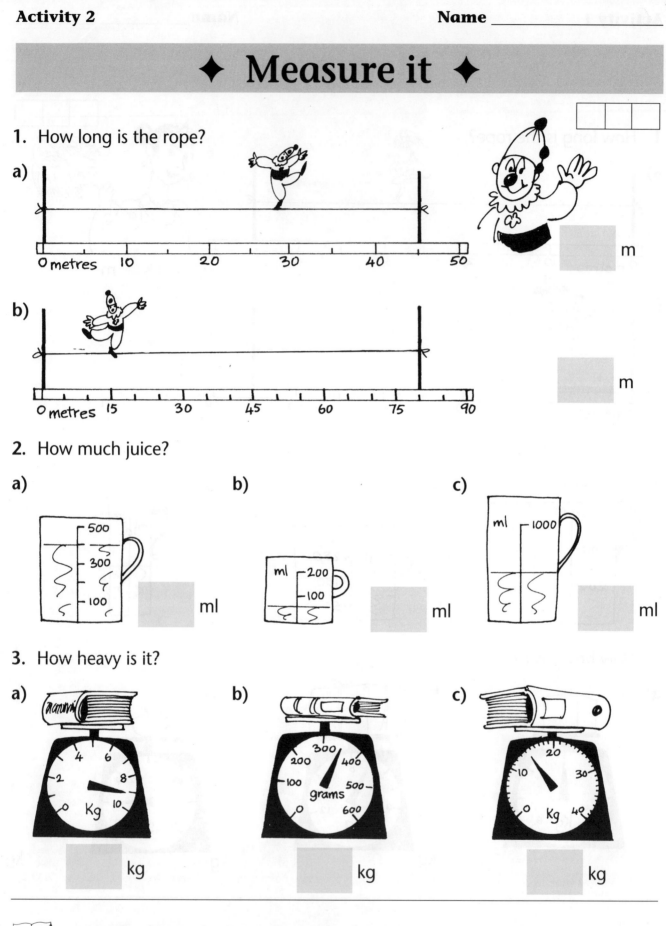

1. How long is the rope?

a)

0 metres   10   20   30   40   50

[ ] m

b)

0 metres 15   30   45   60   75   90

[ ] m

2. How much juice?

a)

500
300
100

[ ] ml

b)

ml 200
100

[ ] ml

c)

ml 1000

[ ] ml

3. How heavy is it?

a)

4 6
2   8
0   10
Kg

[ ] kg

b)

300
200   400
100   500
grams
0   600

[ ] kg

c)

20
10   30
0   Kg   40

[ ] kg

Weigh a heavy book on the scales. Draw the dial and mark
the weight. How heavy is it?

developing
**Numeracy
Skills**

Photocopiable

✦ Measure it ✦

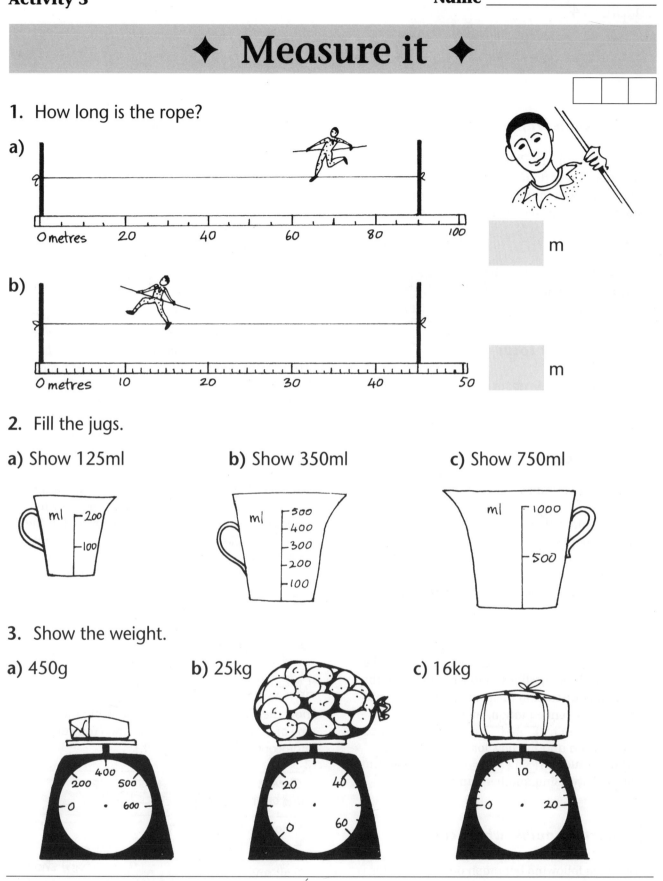

1. How long is the rope?

a)

O metres   20   40   60   80   100

[ ] m

b)

O metres   10   20   30   40   50

[ ] m

2. Fill the jugs.

a) Show 125ml

ml   200

100

b) Show 350ml

ml   500
400
300
200
100

c) Show 750ml

ml   1000

500

3. Show the weight.

a) 450g

400
200   500
0   600

b) 25kg

20   40

0   60

c) 16kg

10

0   20

Weigh a letter on the letter scales. Draw the scales and mark the weight.
How heavy is the letter?

Handling data

◆ Overall learning objectives

◆ Solve problems involving collection, sorting and organisation of data.
◆ Represent data in the form of graphs and charts.
◆ Interpret graphs and charts and make predictions.

◆ LESSON ONE GRAPHS AND CHARTS

◆ Assessment focus

Can the children talk about and interpret data in order to make predictions?

◆ Resources

◆ a selection of graphs from various sources for reference
◆ interlocking cubes
◆ squared paper

◆ Oral work and mental calculation

Mental calculation with 750

◆ Write $100 + \boxed{} = 750$ on the board and ask the children for suggestions as to what to put in the box. After discussing their suggestions, go on to write a different equation, such as $250 + \boxed{} = 750$ and then try $\boxed{} + \boxed{} + \boxed{} = 750$. (You can vary this on another day, for example to an equation such as $\boxed{} + \boxed{} = 750 + \boxed{}$.) Repeat this activity using another number.

◆ Starting point: whole class

◆ Draw the following bar graph on the board (or enlarge it on the photocopier). Explain to the children that it shows all the different fruits that some children had in their lunch boxes one day. The task is to find out what can be learned by

reading this bar graph. Demonstrate to them how it is very like a block graph.

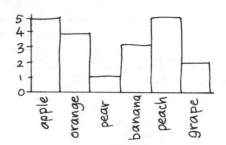

◆ Ask some focused questions such as *"How many different fruits were there?"*, *"Which was the least popular fruit?"*, *"How many more children had peaches than grapes?"* Can the children suggest any other questions? Write some of the questions on the board to help the groups later.
◆ Ask the class if they can say the total number of children in the class, then change the numbers on the left axis to multiples of 2. How does this change the graph?
◆ Tell the three groups they will be using bar graphs very like the one on the board, except they are about the different flavours of crisps sold in the Circus Snacks shop on different days. Say that while they are working you want them to think why the answers they are giving would be useful to the shopkeeper.

◆ Group activities

Focus group

Show the children a pictogram showing the same type of data, such as the one below. (You could photocopy this and enlarge it.)

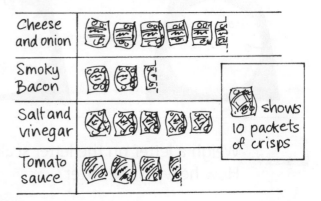

Handling data

Discuss what each picture represents and the fact that half a picture means half the number of packets. Count the total numbers of each variety together and work with the children to help them formulate some questions they could answer using the data. Ask them why this might be an easier graph for finding the total sales than a bar graph. Help them rehearse what they could report to the class about pictograms.

 Teacher-independent groups

Activity sheet 1: The data for this group is shown as a block graph to make counting easier. The aim is for the children to be able to answer the questions and think of one for themselves. This will help them to make some predictions during the plenary session.

LESSON TWO COLLECTING AND REPRESENTING DATA

◆ Assessment focus

Can the children collect and represent numerical data using their choice of chart or table?

◆ Resources

+ cubes
+ 2cm and 1cm squared paper

◆ Oral work and mental calculation

Calculating with 1000

+ Write 1000 on the board. Give the children calculations based on that number.

Activity sheet 2: The data graph on this sheet is shown as a bar chart of the numbers of different crisps but, as for group 1, the children should be encouraged to think hard about the information to be gained from the graph to enable them to make predictions based on the data.

Activity sheet 3: The graph on this sheet uses a scale marked in multiples of 2.

◆ Plenary session

+ Invite the focus group to explain to the others how their graph was different. One or two representatives from the other groups can share the questions they wrote and say how they found the answers. Ask the children why this type of information is helpful to shops. Would the data help the shopkeeper to predict what will happen next day/week?

"What is 10 more than 1000?"
"What is 100 more than 1000?"
"What is 10/100 less than 1000?"
"How many 100s in 1000?
"What is half of 1000?"
"Give me 2 multiples of 100 that add up to 1000.
"Is there a different answer?"
+ Ask them how they solved some of the problems.

◆ Starting point: whole class

+ Remind the class about the different types of graph they have used. Draw some very simple examples on the board, such as block graphs, bar graphs with different scales and pictograms. Say that today they will be collecting some data and showing it on one of those types of graph.
+ Present the children with the situation that Circus Snacks needs their help because they plan to start selling different flavours of ice cream but first they need to find out which is likely to be popular. There is room in their shop for only six flavours.

Handling data

With the children's help write a possible selection on the board. If the list is longer than six options have a show of hands to select the six most popular. Draw a frequency table of the preferred flavours.

Flavour	Liked best
Chocolate	6
Vanilla	3

✦ Say that in their groups they will draw graphs of the data they have just collected and will compare them in the plenary session. Show group 1 how they could model the data using cubes first. Remind them about using the same baseline for each group of blocks.

◆ Group activities

Focus group

Tell this group they will be deciding which drinks Circus Snacks should sell. Help them to decide on six possibilities and to make a tally chart in pairs. Show them how to make a tally. Starting with the data from their table, each pair then asks one table for their preferred option and they must cooperate to make a tally chart of the whole class's preferred drink. Help them to construct a graph using interlocking cubes before they draw one, asking questions about and comparing the numbers.

Teacher-independent groups

Group 1: This group should draw a block graph of the data collected during the introduction. Make 2cm and 1cm squared paper available but model the graph with cubes first.

Group 2: These children should choose the type of graph they will draw using the ice cream data. They then write some of things they can find out from their graph.

Group 3: Delegate to each pair either a pictogram where one picture represents more than one item, for example one ice cream picture represents two children's choices, or a block graph with a vertical scale in 2s. They should use this to draw their diagram and write questions for the plenary session.

◆ Plenary session

✦ Invite group 3 to share their graphs with the class to show different ways of representing the same data. Ask them to explain some of the things they can tell by reading the graph. Use one of the bar graphs drawn by group 2 and compare it with one from group 3. Discuss why this sort of information might be useful to Circus Snacks.

✦ *"We found the favourite flavour of 32 children. Can we predict from that the favourite flavour of the whole school?"*

◆ Further activities

✦ Use the class preferences for foods for a computer database. Can they use it to find, for example, some who like cheese and onion crisps, cola and chocolate ice cream?

◆ Extension

✦ Draw two graphs using the same data, such as 'How Year 3 Come to School', one graph using a scale going in 1s and the other in 2s.

✦ Discuss the similarities and differences made by using the different scales.

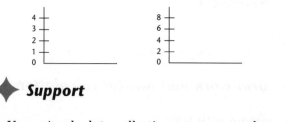

◆ Support

✦ Use a simple data collection program on the computer to draw block graphs to discuss and make predictions from.

86
©Hopscotch Educational Publishing

developing
**Numeracy
Skills**

Numeracy
Year 3/P4

◆ Crisp sales ◆

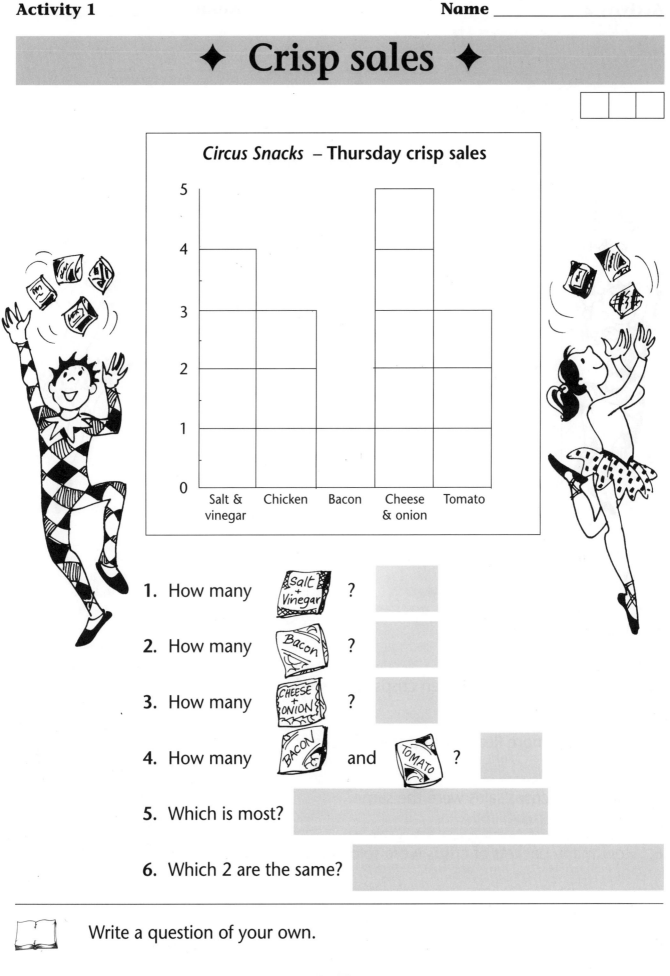

Circus Snacks – Thursday crisp sales

1. How many Salt + Vinegar ?

2. How many Bacon ?

3. How many CHEESE + ONION ?

4. How many BACON and TOMATO ?

5. Which is most?

6. Which 2 are the same?

Write a question of your own.

✦ Crisp sales ✦

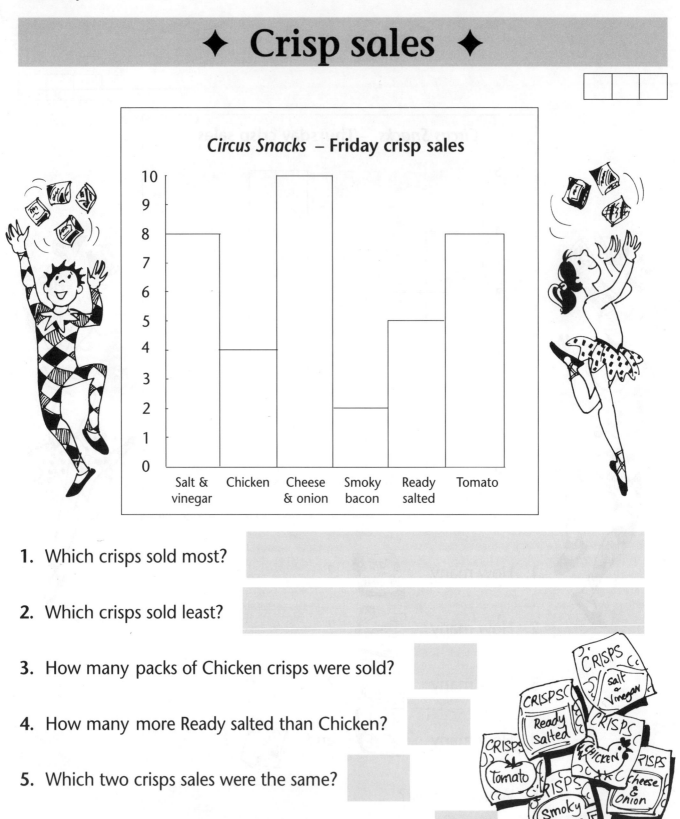

Circus Snacks – Friday crisp sales

Salt & vinegar · Chicken · Cheese & onion · Smoky bacon · Ready salted · Tomato

1. Which crisps sold most?

2. Which crisps sold least?

3. How many packs of Chicken crisps were sold?

4. How many more Ready salted than Chicken?

5. Which two crisps sales were the same?

6. How many packets of crisps were sold altogether?

 Write 2 more questions of your own.

◆ Crisp sales ◆

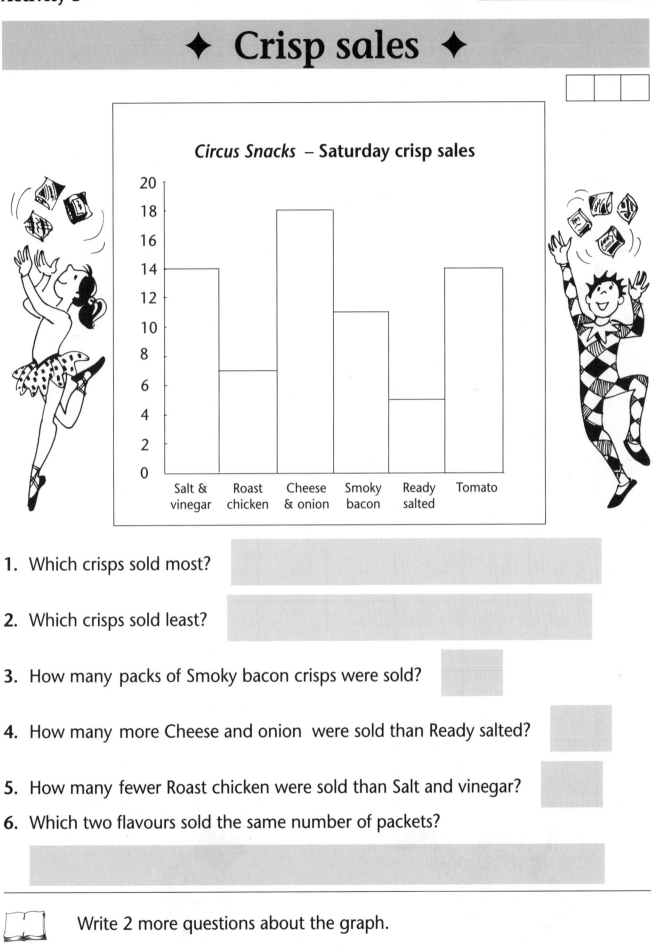

Circus Snacks – **Saturday crisp sales**

1. Which crisps sold most?

2. Which crisps sold least?

3. How many packs of Smoky bacon crisps were sold?

4. How many more Cheese and onion were sold than Ready salted?

5. How many fewer Roast chicken were sold than Salt and vinegar?

6. Which two flavours sold the same number of packets?

Write 2 more questions about the graph.

Name _____

◆ Number square ◆

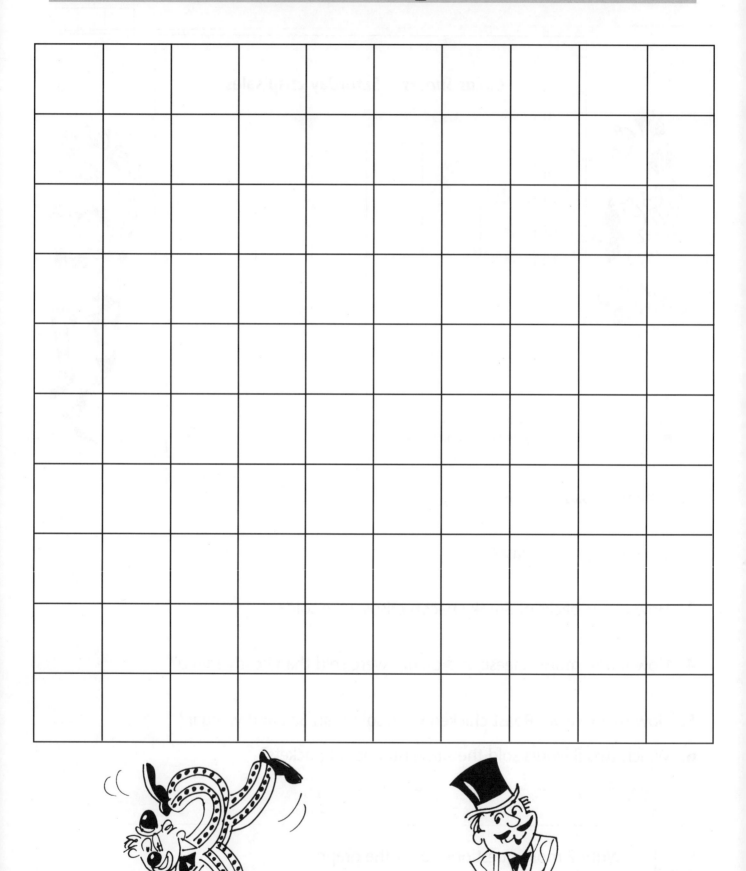

developing
Numeracy
Skills

Photocopiable

Name _____

✦ Number square ✦

0	1	2	3	4	5	6	7	8	9
10	11	12	13	14	15	16	17	18	19
20	21	22	23	24	25	26	27	28	29
30	31	32	33	34	35	36	37	38	39
40	41	42	43	44	45	46	47	48	49
50	51	52	53	54	55	56	57	58	59
60	61	62	63	64	65	66	67	68	69
70	71	72	73	74	75	76	77	78	79
80	81	82	83	84	85	86	87	88	89
90	91	92	93	94	95	96	97	98	99

developing
Numeracy
Skills

✦ Triominoes ✦

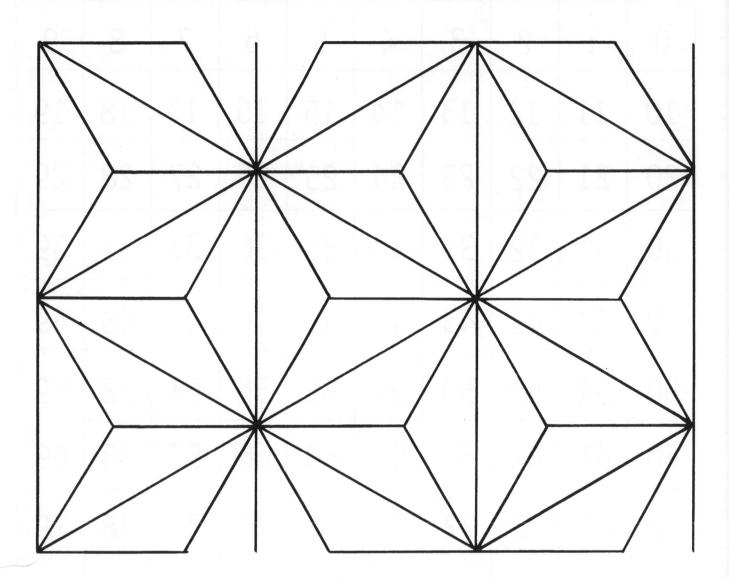

Each piece of this diagram is an equilateral triangle divided into three. The triangles can be cut out along the lines of the equilateral triangles. The challenge is to match the numbers along the equilateral triangle edges. There is a difference of 6 in this example. They could be matched in other ways, for example so that they are equal to 10 (6 and 4, 7 and 3 and so on).

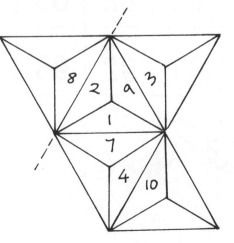

developing
Numeracy
Skills

Photocopiable

Name _____

◆ Triominoes ◆

◆ Work with a partner. Match and colour the triangles with a difference of three.

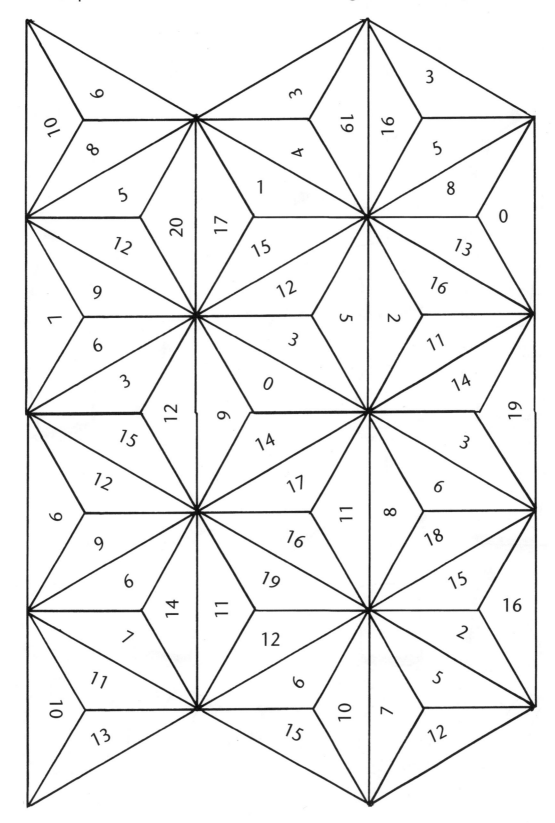

Photocopiable
©Hopscotch Educational Publishing

Name _____

◆ Multiplication game ◆

1. Each player chooses cubes of one colour.
2. Take turns to throw two 0–5 dice.
3. Multiply the two numbers and put a cube on the answer.
4. The player with the most cubes on the clown's hats is the winner.
5. You can have only one cube on each number.

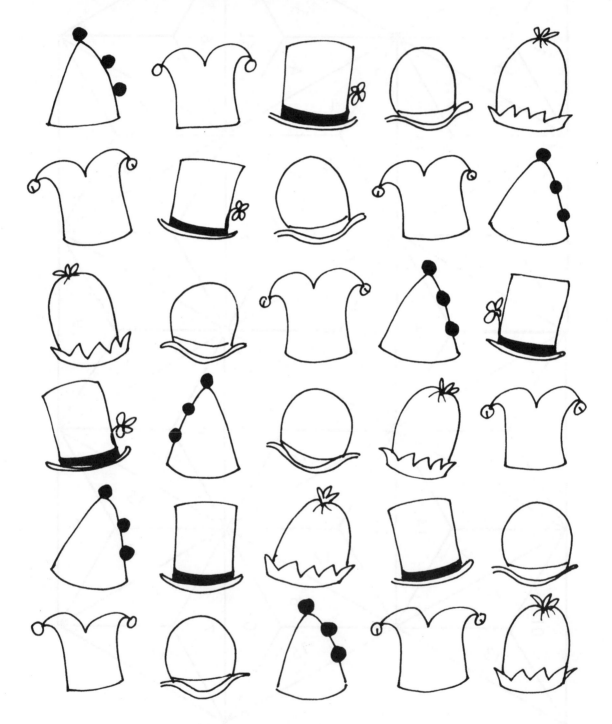

Name _____

◆ Cover the multiples ◆

1. Each player chooses cubes of one colour.
2. Take turns to throw a 0–9 dice.
3. Multiply the number by ☐ and put a cube on the answer.
4. The player with the most cubes on the grid is the winner.
5. You can have only one cube on each number.

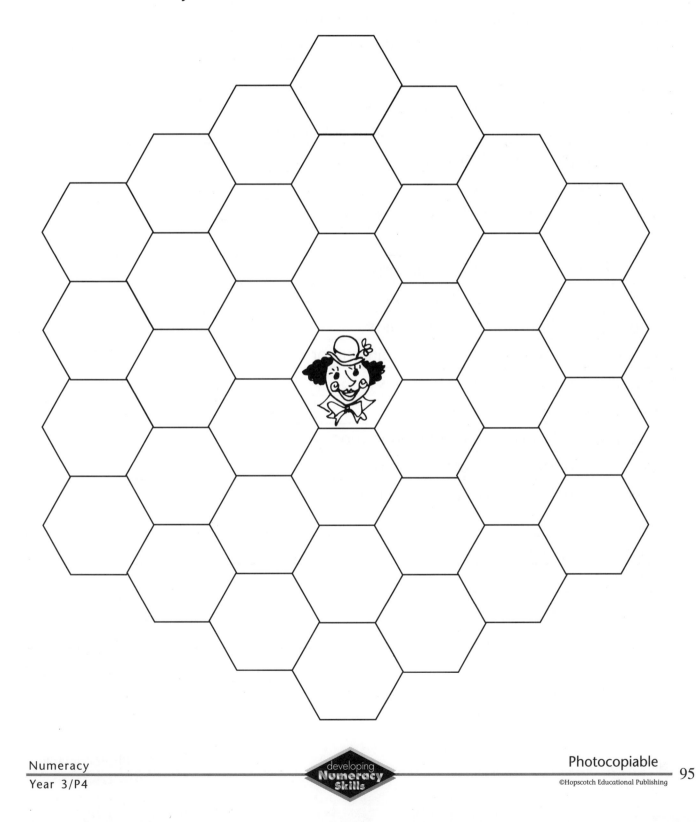

Photocopiable

Name _____

✦ Self assessment sheet ✦

	✔
I can	
use grouping strategies to estimate sensibly and count accurately	
understand rounding to the nearest 10	
describe and extend number sequences	
give a sensible estimate and then check by counting	
add or subtract 1, 10 or 100 from a given number	
order numbers to 1000	
understand and use the relationship between addition and subtraction	
understand that addition can be done in any order	
put the larger number first when adding	
explain how I add and subtract using a number line	
understand that I can find differences by counting on or back	
subtract 10, 9 and 11	
use multiplication in real life problems	
understand that division is the opposite of multiplication	
understand whole number remainders	
make sensible decisions about rounding up or down	
identify and name common fractions	
use a number line for fractions	
recognise and use decimal notation in money	
use rulers etc to solve length problems	
make reasonable estimates and check by measuring	
use suitable units for measuring capacity	
read a variety of scales	
interpret data and make predictions	
collect and represent data	
I can…	
I can…	
I want to get better at…	

Photocopiable

©Hopscotch Educational Publishing